EAT
TO PREVENT
AND CONTROL
DISEASE COOKBOOK

70+ Delicious Indian Vegetarian
Recipes for Healthy Living with
Dedicated Recipes for Diabetes,
Hypertension, and Arthritis

ALSO BY LA FONCEUR

EAT TO PREVENT AND CONTROL DISEASE

Do you know your medicines might make you ill? This book tells how you can reduce your dependence on medicines. Learn how foods that work with the same mechanism as medicines can naturally prevent and control chronic diseases such as diabetes, hypertension, and arthritis.

SECRET OF HEALTHY HAIR

If you are seeking a permanent solution to your hair problems, then Secret of Healthy Hair is for you! Your Complete Food & Lifestyle Guide for Healthy Hair with Season Wise Diet Plans and Hair Care Recipes.

EAT SO WHAT! THE POWER OF VEGETARIANISM

Understand your food scientifically with Eat So What! The Power of Vegetarianism. Learn how you can prevent anemia, vitamin B12, and protein deficiency with vegetarian foods naturally without any man-made dietary supplements.

EAT SO WHAT! SMART WAYS TO STAY HEALTHY

Confused about what to eat and what not to eat for health? Clear your confusion with Eat So What! Smart Ways to Stay Healthy. This book explains the nutritional value of foods, gives direction on what to eat and gives smart tricks and tips to make life healthier.

Dear reader,

The aim of **Eat to Prevent and Control Disease Cookbook** is to help you incorporate superfoods into your diet in such a way that they become part of your regular diet, and you eat them for the taste, not just for health. This cookbook brings you delicious recipes for superfoods that can help you prevent and manage chronic diseases.

Masters of Pharmacy,

Research Scientist,

Registered Pharmacist

Contents

4. EAT FOR MAXIMUM HEALTH BENEFITS

5. EAT TO PREVENT AND CONTROL DIABETES

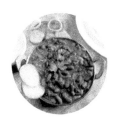

INTRODUCTION

Whether it's the laboratory or the kitchen, it's all about experimenting until you reach the perfect formulation! Not much difference.

From making a perfect formulation in a mortar and pestle

To make the perfect spice blend in a mortar and pestle

It's all about the correct technique! Not much difference.

From following SOPs to following recipes, it's all about the experience that comes from practice. Basics are the same.

The specialty of Indian cooking is that even if you give the same ingredients and the same recipe to different people, the taste of the food prepared by them will be different in all. This is because of the spices involved in Indian cooking. Spices contain volatile oils that give them a distinctive aroma and taste. All spices contain volatile oils, and the roasting and cooking method helps the spices release volatile oils. The amount of volatile oil released can increase or decrease the flavor of food. The way you cook, the cooking time, even the type of flame, low, medium, or high, can all affect the taste of the food. You just need to know the right technique which will make the food most delicious. In this cookbook, you will learn all the techniques to make your food flavorsome. Once you master the techniques, you can start experimenting and doing some additions and omissions in the recipes as per your taste.

Everyone's taste is different. Some like to eat spicy while some prefer mild. Some like to eat gravy, some like dry, and some like curry. All these tastes have been taken care of in this cookbook. You will find all types of food like gravy, dry, and curry in the cookbook, and the spiciness is kept medium. You can adjust the spiciness according to your taste. Apart from this, healthy sweets, snacks, beverages, and tangy dishes are also included in the cookbook, which are delicious as well as nutritious.

Make from scratch! No short cuts

Indian cooking requires very few store-bought items, and the ones that are required can be easily made at home. You will be surprised to know how easily your store-bought items can be made at home. All the recipes in this cookbook are made from scratch. These simple and cost-effective ways can have a tremendous positive impact on your health.

Background of Eat to Prevent and Control Disease Cookbook

Eat to Prevent and Control Disease Cookbook is the second book in the **Eat to Prevent and Control Disease series.** Before moving on to our delectable recipes, here's a brief about *Eat to Prevent and Control Disease book:*

About Eat to Prevent and Control Disease

The book helps reduce your dependence on drugs. It explains foods that boost your immunity, superfoods that can protect you from chronic diseases, foods that reduce oxidative stress and inflammation in your body, and food combinations that can help you maximize health benefits.

Eat to Prevent and Control Disease tells you everything you need to know about the three most common chronic diseases—diabetes, high blood pressure, and arthritis. What foods and lifestyle choices should you avoid and adopt to prevent these diseases? How do your medicines work? What exactly happens in your body in these diseases, and what should be your strategy to prevent and control them. What superfoods mimic your drug's mechanism of action and help lower your blood pressure and sugar levels? What are the key points you should follow to prevent arthritis and get rid of it?

This cookbook brings you delicious ways to incorporate superfoods into your diet that are discussed in *Eat to Prevent and Control Disease.*

The cookbook is completely based on superfoods. Each recipe in this cookbook includes one or more superfoods. In the book *Eat to Prevent and Control Disease,* you learned about the powerful superfoods you should be eating every day. But adding them to your diet doesn't have to be boring. You don't need to eat them forcefully just for the sake of health. This cookbook brings you many delicious and mouth-watering recipes of superfoods that you can eat anytime, any day. These dishes will satisfy your taste buds as well as strengthen your immunity and protect you from chronic diseases with their therapeutic effects.

Eat to Prevent and Control Disease Cookbook is divided into 7 parts, each with different sets of superfood recipes. You will find out how you can boost your immunity with delicious foods.

Certain foods become more nutritious when combined with other foods because they increase the absorption of nutrients into the bloodstream, giving you maximum health benefits. This cookbook provides several tempting recipes for combining the ideal nutrients so that you can get the maximum health benefits from them.

This cookbook has dedicated recipes for diabetes, high blood pressure, and arthritis. You'll learn how to incorporate superfoods into your diet that work in the same way as your medications and naturally prevent and control these diseases so that you can reduce the dosage of your medicines as well as the side effects associated with them. This way, your body heals faster than it typically would. Get ready for a healthy tomorrow!

How to Use Eat to Prevent and Control Disease Cookbook

This cookbook is characterized by

✓ Pure vegetarian recipes

✓ Presence of single or multiple superfoods in recipes

✓ Natural sweeteners wherever possible

✓ Healthier versions of the salt like Himalayan pink rock salt, black salt, kala namak mix, and mineral-rich salt mix

✓ Upgraded whole grains mixed flours

✓ Cold-pressed cooking oil

Cookwares/tools/accessories you need for this cookbook:

· Pressure Cooker

· Hand blender

· Tawa/Skillet

· Muslin cloth

· Steamer

· Convection oven

· Stainless steel kadai/pan

· Mortar and pestle

This cookbook does not use the following ingredients/cooking method/food combinations:

X Canned foods like canned beans

X Refined oil

X Deep frying

X Salt and milk combination

X Refined wheat flour

X Refined white sugar

X Plain salt

X No heating of honey

How to steam cook?

You don't need a steamer to steam vegetables and other foods. You can steam them in a large cooker or pot. For this, you need a stainless steel steamer plate/strainer bowl/colander or any perforated plate or bowl that will fit in the cooker or the pot. Keep in mind that it should be kept 2 to 3 inches above the water. You can use a stainless steel pot stand to keep the perforated plate or bowl above the water.

Type of pressure cooker used:

This cookbook uses regular pressure cooker with pressure regulator weight valve/whistle.

Benefits of using a pressure cooker:

✓ Faster cooking. Saves a lot of time.

✓ Foods retain more nutrition because the steam remains inside and does not escape.

✓ Less messy kitchen.

✓ It can be used as a steamer.

Alternative to pressure cooker: You can cook in a pan covered with a lid, but it will take longer than a pressure cooker.

Healthy Replacements Used in the Cookbook

White Sugar Substitutes

Jaggery, honey, dried fruits, and brown sugar.

White sugar is not used in this cookbook as it provides void calories, which means it has only calories with zero nutrition value. **Eat to Prevent and Control Disease Cookbook** uses jaggery/panela as a sugar substitute because it is the purest form of sugar without any additives and has many health benefits. It is made from sugarcane in an iron vessel, due to which it is an excellent source of iron. If jaggery is not available, you can substitute it with brown sugar. Otherwise, stick to the type of sweetener specified in the recipe for the most authentic flavor.

Jaggery, honey, dried fruits, and brown sugar are healthy alternatives to white sugar. They are nutritious but still are sweet. Consume them in moderation to get maximum health benefits.

Types of Salt Used in the Cookbook

Himalayan pink rock salt, black salt, kala namak mix, and mineral-rich salt mix.

Mineral-rich salt mix: To upgrade your regular salt, mix Himalayan pink rock salt with your regular salt in 1:1 ratio. Use this mineral-rich salt for better health. Regular salt contains only sodium, whereas Himalayan rock salt is unprocessed and contains traces of iron, magnesium, calcium, and other minerals.

Mineral-rich salt mix is used in all the recipes in this cookbook. Wherever salt is mentioned, it refers to mineral-rich salt mix.

Types of Fat Used in the Cookbook

Mustard oil, extra virgin olive oil, sesame oil, cow ghee, and nuts.

Mustard Oil

Is it banned?

Mustard oil is one of the main cooking oils in many parts of the world, including but not limited to India (particularly North India and West Bengal), Nepal, and Bangladesh. Mustard oil has been used for cooking here for thousands of years, but it is banned in USA, European Union, and Canada for edible purposes. All commercially available mustard oils in these countries are labeled *"For external use only."*

The reason for the ban is the presence of erucic acid in mustard oil. Animal studies suggest that high intake of erucic acid is associated with heart diseases. However, this association has not been established for humans as all studies have been done on laboratory animals, and no actual research has been carried on humans. So far, no cases of any harmful effects due to exposure to erucic acid have been reported in humans.

In Indian cooking, mustard oil is used for cooking as well as for dressing. When using mustard oil for cooking, always choose cold-pressed mustard oil instead of refined one to get maximum health benefits.

Substitute of mustard oil

For cooking: Canola oil (but it's refined oil, not pressed oil).

For dressing: Sesame oil or any other cold-pressed oil.

Extra Virgin Olive Oil

To cook or not to cook extra virgin olive oil?

If you cook oil beyond its smoke point, it degrades, and its chemical composition changes. This releases harmful chemicals that get absorbed into the food. It is a myth that extra virgin olive oil can only be used in dressing and not in cooking. The smoke point of extra virgin olive oil is 207 °C. It was believed that extra virgin olive oil oxidizes when cooked due to its low smoke point, but research studies have proven this to be wrong. Everyday cooking doesn't reach 207 °C. Extra virgin olive oil is safe for all types of cooking except for deep frying.

Types of Flour Used in the Cookbook

Whole wheat flour mixed with barley flour, oats flour made from oats groats, amaranth flour, gram flour, and semolina.

Whole Wheat Barley Mixed Flour

All recipes in this cookbook use whole wheat flour mixed with barley flour. Wherever whole wheat flour is mentioned, it refers to whole wheat flour mixed with barley flour.

Why Barley?

Barley is an excellent source of soluble fiber and antioxidant minerals such as magnesium, copper, selenium, and chromium. Carbohydrates present in barley convert to glucose slowly, without rapidly increasing blood sugar levels. It increases a hormone that helps reduce chronic low-grade inflammation, thus protecting against many chronic diseases as inflammation is the leading cause of cancer, diabetes, arthritis, and many other chronic diseases. If you want to prevent diabetes, then start eating barley regularly.

To make Whole Wheat Barley Mixed Flour: Mix barley flour in the ratio of 1:7 to whole wheat flour. Add 100 grams of barley flour to 700 grams of wheat flour and mix it well. Use this upgraded whole wheat flour instead of regular wheat flour.

Oat Flour

All recipes in this cookbook use oat flour made from oats groats. Wherever oat flour is mentioned, it refers to oat flour made from oat groats until and unless specified otherwise.

Oat groats are the purest form of oats. It looks similar to whole wheat but is slightly thinner in shape. These are the least processed and highest in nutritional value. The most common type of oats is rolled oats, which have the least nutrition because this variety is the most processed one, and most of the nutrition is lost while processing. They are easy to digest and sometimes fortified (manually added) with essential vitamins and minerals lost during processing, but they are not as healthy and natural as oats groats.

Oat groats are the most nutritious, and even a small intake is enough to provide you with essential nutrients. But they are heavy to digest, so if you eat more, you will feel heaviness in the stomach. So do not eat them too much at a time. Recipes in this cookbook have taken care of the oats amount sufficient for easy digestion and fulfilling nutritional requirements.

If you buy oat groats, once open, consume them within three months. Otherwise, they get spoiled. To grind oats to make oat flour, you need a high-power grinder (above 750 w). Low power mixer grinder will result in coarser flour. You can store oat flour for one month.

For vegan options: Some of the recipes in this cookbook are vegan, but most are vegetarian. You can replace milk and honey with plant-based milk and sweeteners, respectively.

For gluten-free options: Replace wheat, barley, and semolina with any gluten-free flour. The result will be similar without affecting the overall taste of the dish.

Moderation is the key. Whether you're using the healthy options of sugar, salt, or fat, consuming too much of these can negatively affect your health. Although they are healthy options, consuming them in excess will nullify their good effects. So consume them in moderation.

Conversions

Degree Celcius to Fahrenheit	Metric Conversion
160 °C = 320 °F	1000 Grams = 1 Kilogram
180 °C = 356 °F	1 Kilogram = 2.2 Pounds
200 °C = 392 °F	1000 Milliliter = 1 Liter
220 °C = 428 °F	28.34 Grams = 1 Ounce

Symbols

Unit	Symbol	Unit	Symbol
Liter	L	Tablespoon	tbsp
Milliliter	ml	Teaspoon	tsp
Gram	g	Degree Celcius	°C
Minute	min	Inch	in

Cup sizes vary from country to country. Therefore, to make it easier to understand, all measurements are given in metric. In general, in this cookbook, 50 grams equals a quarter cup, 100 grams equals a half-cup, and 200 grams equals 1 cup.

Even though cup size varies from country to country, teaspoon and tablespoon sizes are same everywhere. Where quantities are less, the recipes in this cookbook use teaspoons and tablespoons to specify amounts.

1 teaspoon: 5 g | 1 tablespoon: 10 g

In some recipes like masala and mixed dal fry, the ingredients must be mixed in a specific proportion. In these recipes, quantities are given in tablespoons, not metric, to provide accurate ratios.

In general, one tablespoon equals 10 grams, but the actual amount varies according to the ingredients. For example, one tablespoon of coriander seeds contains less than 10 grams. In recipes such as garam masala and panch phoran, where the quantities are specified in teaspoons or tablespoons, they are specified considering their actual weight.

INDIAN COOKING

Eat to Prevent and Control Disease Cookbook's recipes are easy to cook and less time-consuming, you can cook them every day. However, some recipes may take some time to prepare. You can cook them on the weekend when you have a little extra time to invest in cooking. Dishes that are heavy and which keep you full till evening are marked as weekend special in the cookbook.

Let's understand a little more about Indian cooking:

Types of Indian Subji

Dry Subji: Dry subji is called *bhujia subji,* which is served as the second subji option in the main course.

Gravy: Gravy subjis are richer and often creamer. These types of *subjis* are thick and contain nut fats like cashews, melon seeds and peanuts. Gravy subjis taste better when you eat them with raw onions. This is the reason why they are always served with raw onions and lemon. This type of subji is served on special occasions, like when you have visiting guests at your home or when you want to make your Sunday special.

Curry: Curry is called *Rasedar subji,* which is thinner than gravy and has more *Ras* means it contains more water. These are the most common types of subji served in the main course. It may or may not be full of fat. When cooking a rich version on a special occasion, it usually has a high amount of ghee or butter. In this cookbook, you'll find curry-type subjis that don't require high fat and can be eaten guilt-free any day.

The Right Way of Cooking for Enhanced Taste

The right way of cooking gravy

The cooking time is very important while making gravy. In the gravy, the onion-ginger-garlic mixture should be cooked to such an extent that all the rawness of the onion is removed. The nuts should be cooked to a point till the gravy leaves oil. Cook on low or medium-low flame. If you cook on high flame or medium flame, then the mixture will dry quickly, and the gravy will not release oil. If the gravy is not cooked well, then the taste of the gravy will be bland and unbalanced.

The right way of cooking rasedar/curry

Curries/rasedar often do not contain nut fat and are the easiest type of cooking. In this, the spices should be cooked well on low flame for a long time. Once the onions and tomatoes are cooked, add masala and cook on low flame for a long time. It helps to develop the taste. When the masala is cooked well, add water and vegetables to it, bring it to a boil and simmer for 10 minutes on low flame.

The right way to roast nuts/oats

Dry roast while stirring continuously on low flame. Nuts/oats should be roasted until they change color slightly, not until they turn brown or start burning. Turn off the flame and leave them in a pan for 5 minutes. They continue to cook even after turning off the flame in the hot pan.

The right way of roasting whole spices

Roast the whole spices on low flame while stirring continuously until the spices release an aromatic smell.

Tips for enhancing flavor and maximizing health benefits

- To enhance the taste of dry fruits, roast them. It gives a heavenly taste if you roast dry fruits in ghee, whether in as little as half or 1 teaspoon ghee. But it is important to use homemade ghee for roasting as they are rich in flavor and purer than store-bought ghee.

- Soak the beans overnight to reduce the amount of phytic acid, the anti-nutrient of the beans. This helps your body absorb more nutrients from the beans.

- Consumption of beans can cause bloating and flatulence. To avoid such problems, boil the beans thoroughly before using them. Also, add about ¾th to 1 tsp asafoetida while cooking. It helps prevent bloating and flatulence caused by beans.

- If you are using whole spices, then roast them before adding them for better taste. This will enhance their taste.

- Soak the rice in enough water for fifteen minutes before cooking. This shortens the cooking time and lowers the phytic acid content of the rice.

- Preheat the oven to cook evenly. It also reduces the overall cooking time.

Keep Handy!

For Indian cooking, keep the following species always ready with you:

Kashmiri red chili powder is characterized by dark red color and is less spicy. This not only gives a bright red color to the food but also keeps the food less spicy.

Fenugreek seeds powder: Dry roast the fenugreek seeds till their color starts changing. Cool them and grind them into a coarse powder.

Coriander powder: Dry roast the whole coriander seeds till they slightly change color. Let them cool down. Grind into a fine powder.

Cumin powder: Dry roast the cumin seeds till they slightly change color. Cool them and grind them finely.

Coriander-cumin powder: For more ease, mix coriander powder and cumin powder in the ratio of 2:1. Mix 50 g cumin powder with 100 g coriander powder and use this mixture instead of coriander powder.

Dry mango powder (*Amchur*): Dry mango powder is made from finely grinding the dry raw mangoes.

Garam masala: This is the most commonly used spice in Indian cooking. Find the recipe in the next chapter.

2

Everything

at Home!

Preparation of Indian cuisine requires very few store-bought items. Almost everything can be made at home. Like ghee, curd, and various spices are readily available in the market, but they can be easily made at home. It is an easy and cost-effective method, and once you know the technique, you do not need much expertise.

Here are the add-on recipes necessary to prepare the main dishes of this cookbook. These are either served with meals or are used in cooking to enhance the taste of the food.

Kala Namak Mix

Makes: 440 g
Prep time: 20 mins

Ingredients

Black salt:	200 g
Roasted cumin seeds:	50 g
Black pepper:	25 g
Cloves:	10
Rock salt:	100 g
Roasted carom seeds:	50 g
Asafoetida:	5 g
Green cardamom:	5

Method

1. Dry roast cumin seeds and carom seeds.
2. If you are using whole black salt and rock salt, then crush black salt and rock salt with the help of a pestle.
3. Grind cumin, carom seeds, black pepper, cloves, cardamom, and asafoetida together.
4. Add black salt and rock salt and grind again into fine powder.
5. Store in an airtight container for up to two months. Do not open the lid frequently to keep the kala namak mix fresh.
6. Fill the Kala Namak Mix in a small salt sprinkler for daily use.

MASALA

Masale/spices are an integral part of Indian cooking. These spices have medicinal and therapeutic effects. They help in maintaining the normal functioning of the body. Different spices have different effects on the body. For example, coriander and fennel are good for digestion, while cardamom helps remove toxins from the body. Spices contain flavonoids, a type of antioxidant that helps prevent chronic diseases such as heart disease, diabetes, and cancer.

Spices are warm in nature and produce heat in the body. Eating them in large quantities in winter keeps you warm, while the consumption of spices should be moderate in summer.

The most common masale used in Indian cooking are garam masala, chole masala, and panch phoran. These masale will be used in the recipes of the **Eat to Prevent and Control Disease Cookbook.** These spice blends are readily available in the market, but making them in the home ensures you eat a fresh, flavorsome, and pure form of masala, giving your food the most authentic taste and maximum health benefits.

Garam Masala

Makes: 70 g
Prep time: 15 mins
Cooking time: 5 mins

Ingredients

Coriander seeds:	3 tbsp
Cumin seeds:	2 tbsp
Black pepper:	1 tbsp
Fennel:	1 tbsp
Dried ginger:	1 inch
Cloves:	8
Black cardamom:	2
Green cardamom:	6
Nutmeg:	½ small
Mace:	Half shreds
Bay leaf:	4
Cinnamon stick:	2 inches
Star anise:	1 in
Carom seeds:	½ tsp
Caraway seeds:	¼ tsp

Method

1. Dry roast all the ingredients on low flame for 5-7 minutes until your kitchen fills with aromatic spices smell.
2. Turn off the flame. Let the spices cool down.
3. Finely grind the spices. Store garam masala in an airtight container to keep it fresh for longer.

Uses: Almost in all types of food from curry to gravy, from cutlets to dal fry.

Note: It is not that if any of the ingredients are not available, then you cannot make garam masala. If an ingredient is not available, skip it. This will slightly change the taste but is still be better than store-bought garam masala.

Chole Masala Powder

Makes: 110 g | Prep time: 15 mins | Cooking time: 5 mins

Ingredients

Coriander seeds:	4 tbsp		Cumin seeds:	2 tbsp
Black pepper:	2 tbsp		Black salt:	1½ tbsp
Dried ginger:	2 inches		Cloves:	10
Black cardamom:	2		Green cardamom:	6
Nutmeg:	1 small		Dry red chilies:	6
Bay leaf:	4 medium or 3 large		Cinnamon:	2 inches
Dried fenugreek leaves:	2 tbsp		Dried mint leaves:	1 tsp
Turmeric powder:	1 tbsp		Dry mango powder:	1½ tbsp

Method

1. Mix turmeric powder, dry mango powder, and black salt. Keep aside.
2. Dry roast the rest of all the ingredients on low flame till spices release an aromatic smell.
3. Grind the roasted spices to a fine powder. Add turmeric powder, dry mango powder, and black salt to it. Mix well. Store in an airtight container.

Uses: Chole masala powder is the main masala used in chole masala and brown chickpeas masala subji.

Panch Phoran

Makes: 70 g | Prep time: 10 mins | Cooking time: 5 mins

Ingredients

Coriander seeds:	4 tbsp	Fennel seeds:	2 tbsp
Fenugreek seeds:	1 tbsp	Whole dry red chilies:	2
Nigella seeds:	1 tsp	Mustard seeds:	1 tsp

Method

1. Remove the stem from chilies. If you want to make the chilies less spicy, remove the seeds.
2. Dry roast all ingredients except mustard seeds till the spices release an aromatic smell.
3. Cool the spices. Add mustard seeds and grind them finely.
4. Store Panch Phoran in an airtight container.

Uses: Panch phoran is used in stuffed vegetables such as stuffed bell pepper, stuffed bitter gourd, and stuffed pointed gourd.

MILK PRODUCTS

There is not only one way to make ghee at home. Ghee can be made from malai (cream top of milk), butter, and curd. Using cow's milk to make ghee is a great way to boost your health. Cow's milk ghee has a high smoke point, making it safe for cooking that requires high temperatures, such as deep-frying. Including ghee in your diet is beneficial when you replace other forms of fat with ghee, not when you take ghee as an additional source of fat. To get the complete nutrition of ghee, replace butter, margarine with ghee.

Desi Ghee

Makes: 125 ml | Prep time: 7-10 days | Cooking time: 45 mins

Ingredients

Cream top of cow's milk:	500 g

Method

1. Boil 2 liters of milk. Turn off the flame. Let it cool down completely.

2. After 4-5 hours, you will see a thick layer of cream (malai) on the top of the milk. Collect this cream and store it in an airtight container in the freezer.

3. Repeat this every day till you collect 500 g of cream. It will take around 7 to 10 days. Days may vary due to the quality and quantity of milk. Be sure to keep it in the freezer in an airtight container.

4. To make ghee, take it out from the freezer and leave it for 3-4 hours till it comes to room temperature. Now using a hand blender, blend the cream so that it becomes smooth and uniform.

5. Take a pan and pour smooth cream into it. Bring it to a boil and let it boil for about half an hour till the transparent ghee starts separating.

6. Let it boil for another 15 to 20 minutes till the ghee separates completely and the milk solids turn brown. Stir continuously.

7. Turn off the flame. Leave for 15 minutes. Strain the ghee, discard the solid brown part and collect the ghee in a container. Use as required.

Tip: Usually, the cream is whipped until butter and buttermilk separate, and butter is used to make ghee, but this results in yellow-colored thin ghee. To make granular ghee, it is necessary to blend the cream until it is smooth and uniform, not until butter starts separating.

Low Fat Thick Curd

Makes: 750 g | Prep time: 8 hours | Cooking time: 10 mins

Ingredients

Skimmed cow's milk:	1 L
Curd starter:	1 tsp

Method

1. Blend curd with a spoon for 2-3 minutes to make it smooth.

2. Boil the milk for 10 minutes. Let the milk cool down. To make perfect thick curd, keep the milk lukewarm, neither completely cold nor too hot. Add curd in lukewarm milk and mix well.

3. Cover with a lid and keep it in a warm and dry place overnight. To make it even more fat-free, remove the layer of cream from the top of the curd the following day.

4. If you need the curd on the same day, pre-heat the oven at 160 °C for 5 to 10 minutes. Switch off the oven. Put the covered curd in the hot oven for 3-4 hours. Your low-fat curd is ready. Take out a tablespoon of curd for future batches and use the rest of the curd as needed.

Hung curd

1. Put the curd in a muslin cloth and tie it. Squeeze lightly to remove excess water. Hang it on a tap or any other place for 5-6 hours.

2. Take out the hung curd in a bowl. Blend with a spoon for 2 minutes. Your creamy hung curd is ready.

Tips:

1. Curd starter is nothing but leftover curd from the first batch of curd making. If you are making curd for the first time at home, you can buy a curd starter from a dairy shop, or any other store-bought curd will work as well.

2. Do not add too much curd starter to the milk. The more curd starter you add, the more sour your curd will be.

CHUTNEY

Chutneys are the dip used with an evening snack, paratha, or added to a dish to enhance the taste.

Green Chutney

Makes: 200 ml | Prep time: 15 mins

Ingredients

Coriander leaves:	100 g
Garlic/Green garlic:	25 g
Ginger:	½ inch
Green chilies:	4
Dry mango powder:	½ tsp
Salt:	To taste
Water:	75 ml

Method

1. Grind all the ingredients except salt in 25 ml water.

2. Add salt and the rest of the water. Mix well.

3. Store in an airtight container in the refrigerator for up to 2 weeks.

Red Garlic Chutney

Makes: 60 ml | Prep time: 10 mins

Ingredients

Garlic:	15 cloves
Red chili powder:	1 tbsp
Water:	50 ml
Salt:	To taste

Method

1. Grind all the ingredients together except salt.

2. Add salt and store in the refrigerator for up to 5 days.

Khunua

Makes: 20 g | Prep time: 15 mins

Ingredients

Garlic:	15-20 cloves
Green chilies:	3
Salt:	To taste
Mustard oil:	1 tsp

Method

1. Roughly chop green chilies. Put garlic and chilies in a mortar and crush them using the pestle.

2. Fill it in an airtight container. Add salt and mustard oil and mix well. Store in the refrigerator for up to 5 days.

Eat to Boost
Immunity

As we have covered the immunity-boosting superfoods in detail in *Eat to Prevent and Control Disease,* we will now see how you can incorporate those superfoods into your diet in this cookbook.

This chapter focuses on foods that boost immunity as well as superfoods that have therapeutic and medicinal effects on the body. The superfoods on which the recipes of this chapter are based are:

- Green tea.

- Herbs that have therapeutic effects: **Turmeric, fenugreek seeds,** and **basil leaves.**

- Nutrient-dense vegetables and legumes: **Sweet potato** and **mung sprouts.**

- Vitamin C-rich foods: **Red** and **green bell pepper.**

- Foods rich in vitamin A: **Sweet potato.**

- Omega-3 fats and zinc-rich foods: **Cashew nuts, almonds, walnuts, flax seeds, etc.**

The Ultimate Green Tea Kadha

Taking kadha every day supports immune system and protects against the common cold, viral infections, and flu. Start your day with a cup of the ultimate green tea kadha and see for yourself how less you get sick.

Serves: 4 | Prep time: 5 mins | Cooking time: 10 mins | Beverage

Ingredients

Green tea:	4 tsp		Fresh turmeric:	1½ inches
Carom seeds:	1 tsp		Fresh ginger:	1½ inches
Cloves:	6		Cinnamon:	½ inch
Bay leaf:	1		Basil leaves:	10
Black pepper:	6		Water:	900 ml

Method

1. Take all the ingredients except green tea and water in a mortar and crush them using a pestle. Put the herbs in a pan and add water.

2. Bring the kadha to a boil. Simmer for 5 minutes on medium flame.

3. Add green tea and simmer for 5-8 minutes or till the kadha reduces to 600 ml. Turn off the flame. Strain kadha and drink hot.

Tip: If you want to make the kadha sweet, then add jaggery while simmering. If you have a cold, sore throat, or cough, take the kadha three times a day, do not add any sweet, and increase the quantity of black pepper to 10. Take a sip, tighten your lips and exhale through your nose. This will help in relieving nasal congestion.

Dry Fruits Milk

Serves: 4
Prep time: 5 mins
Cooking time 20 mins
Beverage

Ingredients

Dried coconut:	50 g
Poppy seeds:	10 g
Dried dates:	50 g
Almond:	50 g
Cashew nuts:	50 g
Walnut:	30 g
Pumpkin seeds:	20 g
Fox nuts:	20 g
Water:	150 ml
Ghee:	½ tsp
Milk:	1.5 L

Method

1. Soak all dry fruits in enough water overnight. Soak poppy seeds separately.
2. Drain the water and rinse the dry fruits with fresh water.
3. Remove seeds from dried dates. Grind all the ingredients together with 150 ml of water.
4. Heat ghee in a pan. Add dry fruits paste to it. Cook for 5 to 10 minutes or until all water is evaporated. It will look like halwa at this stage. Turn off the flame. You can also eat it as halwa.
5. Boil milk in a separate saucepan. Add dry fruit halwa in milk as required. Mix well. Simmer for 5 minutes.
6. Cool the Dry Fruits Milk. Stir with a spoon and serve hot.

Golden Milk

Serves: 4 | Prep time: 5 mins | Cooking time: 10 mins | Beverage

Ingredients

Fresh turmeric:	2 inches
or Turmeric powder:	1 tbsp
Milk:	1 L

Method

1. Boil the milk.
2. Peel the fresh turmeric and crush it in a mortar with the help of a pestle.
3. Add crushed fresh turmeric to the milk. Simmer for 5 minutes. Turn off the flame. Strain the milk. Let it cool down.
4. Drink it just before bed while the golden milk is still hot.

Tip: Use fresh turmeric in the winter season and turmeric powder in other seasons when fresh turmeric is not available. Drink hot golden milk every day in the winter season.

Tulsi Summer Drink

Serves: 4 | Prep time: 15 mins | Beverage

Ingredients

Indian Tulsi/Basil leaves:	50
Ginger:	2 inches
Green chilies:	2
Cumin seeds:	1 tbsp
Lemon juice::	2 tbsp
Chilled water:	1 L
Kala namak mix:	To taste

Method

1. Roast cumin seeds till they slightly change color.
2. Take basil leaves, ginger, chilies, and roasted cumin seeds in a grinder jar. Grind with about 50 ml water to a fine paste.
3. Pass the paste through a strainer. Discard the solid part.
4. Add the remaining water, kala namak mix, and lemon juice.
5. Chill tulsi summer drink in the refrigerator for 2 hours.
6. Enjoy the tangy Tulsi Summer Drink on a hot afternoon.

Bell Pepper Chutney

Makes: 200 g
Prep time: 15 mins
Cooking time: 25 mins
Condiment

Ingredients

Red bell pepper:	1 large/160 g	Green bell pepper:	1 small/50 g
Apple cider vinegar:	1 tbsp	Black pepper powder:	½ tsp
Jaggery:	20 g	Cloves:	6
Chopped onion:	1 large	Chopped ginger:	1 tbsp
Chopped garlic:	2 tbsp	Bay leaf:	1
Kashmiri red chili powder:	1 tbsp	Salt:	To taste
Sesame oil:	1½ tbsp	Water:	200 ml

Method

1. Place a metal rack over a stove-top burner over direct flame. Put red and green bell pepper on the metal rack and roast on low flame.

2. Rotate and roast the bell peppers from all sides. It will take around 10-15 minutes. Take them off the flame.

3. Take bell peppers in a bowl and pour 100 ml hot water over them. Cover with a lid and keep aside for 15 minutes.

4. Blend bell peppers with water to a smooth paste. Keep aside.

5. Heat oil in a pan. Add bay leaf, cloves, ginger, and garlic. Cook on medium flame till they start turning brown.

6. Add chopped onions and cook for 6-8 minutes.

7. Add Kashmiri red chili powder and cook for 30 seconds.

8. Add bell pepper paste. Mix well and cook for 5 minutes.

9. Add salt, black pepper, jaggery, and apple cider vinegar. Mix well.

10. Add 100 ml water. Cover the chutney with a lid and cook for 10 minutes on low flame. Stir occasionally.

11. When oil appears on the top of the chutney, it means that the chutney is ready. Turn off the flame and let the chutney cool down.

12. Fill it in an airtight glass container and store it in the refrigerator for up to 2 weeks.

13. Serve the Bell Pepper Chutney with cutlet or as a dip or spread over bread and chapati or use in veg rolls.

Methi Pyaz Paratha

Serves: 4
Prep time: 30 mins
Cooking time: 20 mins
Breakfast

Ingredients

Whole wheat flour:	400 g
Onion:	4 ½ medium
Nigella seeds:	½ tsp
Roasted cumin seeds:	1 tsp
Coriander leaves:	20 g
Extra virgin olive oil:	2 tbsp
Sprouted fenugreek seeds:	40 g
Carom seeds:	1 tsp
Green chilies:	2
Salt:	To taste
Asafoetida:	¼ tsp
Water:	100 ml

Method

1. Grind sprouted fenugreek seeds with 100 ml of water.

2. Dry roast cumin seeds. Crush them in a mortar with a pestle.

3. Finely chop onion and green chilies.

4. Take all ingredients in a bowl except oil and knead to make a stiff dough without adding any additional water. If it seems too dry, add 2 tbsp of water. Make sure not to add too much water as the onion will release water later. Cover and rest the dough for 15 minutes.

5. Take one dough ball, dip it in the dry whole wheat flour, and dust off the excess flour. Use a rolling pin to roll the dough into a circle.

6. Heat the pan/griddle/skillet (Tawa) on medium-high flame. Place the paratha on the tawa. Cook for about a minute or until the paratha starts puffing from the base in some places.

7. Flip the paratha and spread 3-4 drops of olive oil. Cook for 2 minutes until lightly browned.

8. Flip the paratha again and pour 3-4 drops of olive oil on top, and spread it evenly over the surface. Press the paratha gently with a flat spatula so that the paratha gets cooked evenly.

9. Once brown spots appear on both sides of the paratha, take it out on a serving plate. Similarly, make all the parathas.

10. Enjoy Methi Pyaz Paratha with red chutney, green chutney, and curd.

Sprouted Mung Bean Subji

Serves: 4 | Prep time: 15 mins | Cooking time: 30 mins | Side dish

Ingredients

Sprouted mung beans:	250 g	Onion:	2 medium
Tomato:	2 medium	Ginger:	1 inch
Garlic:	6 cloves	Whole red chilies:	2
Mustard seeds:	1 tsp	Cumin seeds:	½ tsp
Coriander-cumin powder:	1½ tsp	Garam masala:	½ tsp
		Asafoetida:	½ tsp
Jaggery:	15 g	Turmeric powder:	½ tsp
Bay leaf:	1	Oil:	1 tbsp
Water:	350 ml	Salt:	To taste

Method

1. Heat oil in a pan. Add asafoetida, bay leaf, red chilies, mustard seeds, and cumin seeds. Cook till mustard seeds start crackling.

2. Add ginger and garlic. Cook for 2 minutes. Add chopped onions. Cook on low flame for 5-7 minutes.

3. Add turmeric powder, garam masala, coriander-cumin powder. Mix well. Cover and cook for 5 minutes on low flame.

4. Add chopped tomatoes and salt. Cook for 5 minutes.

5. Add sprouted mung beans. Mix well and cook for 5 minutes.

6. Add water and jaggery. Cover and cook for 10 minutes on low flame. Serve hot.

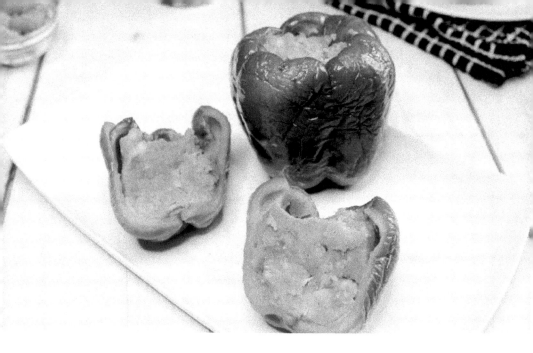

Stuffed Bell Pepper

Serves: 4 | Prep time: 15 mins | Cooking time: 40 mins | Main course

Ingredients

Green bell pepper:	4 large	Sweet potato:	600 g
Red chili powder:	½ tsp	Chopped ginger:	1 tsp
Chopped garlic:	1 tbsp	Dry mango powder:	½ tsp
Cumin seeds:	½ tsp	Asafoetida:	¼ tsp
Panch phoran:	1 ½ tsp	Salt:	To taste

Method

1. Steam the sweet potatoes. Remove the skin and mash them.

2. Heat oil in a pan. Add asafoetida and cumin seeds. When cumin seeds start turning brown, add ginger and garlic. Cook for 2 minutes. Add mashed sweet potatoes. Mix well and cook for 5 minutes.

3. Add salt, dry mango powder, red chili powder, and panch phoran masala. Mix well. Cook for 10 minutes on medium flame. Stir occasionally. Turn off the flame and let the stuffing cool down.

4. Wash the bell peppers and remove the top portion and seeds.

5. Stuff the sweet potato mixture in each bell pepper. Brush each bell pepper with oil. Sprinkle salt over each bell pepper.

6. Place the stuffed bell peppers in a metal rack and bake in a pre-heated oven at 180 °C for 15 minutes. Flip the bell peppers and bake again for another 10-15 minutes.

Sweet Potato Burfi

Serves: 4
Prep time: 20 mins
Cooking time: 40 mins
Dessert

Ingredients

Sweet potato:	300 g (purple variety)
Water:	100 ml
Almond:	10 -15
Jaggery:	60-70 g
Ghee:	1 tbsp

Method

1. Steam cook sweet potatoes. Remove skin and mash them using a potato masher or spoon.

2. Put jaggery in a pan. Heat it on low flame. When it starts melting, add water to it.

3. Turn the flame to medium and let the mix boil till one string chashni is formed. To check, put a drop of jaggery chashni on a plate. Let it cool down for 15 seconds. Take it between your thumb and index finger and check if it forms a string while separating your fingers. If it forms a string, it means it is done. If not, cook for another minute and check again.

4. Turn the flame to low and add mashed sweet potatoes and mix well. Keep stirring it continuously so that it does not stick to the bottom. Once mixed well, cook it on low to medium flame.

5. It will start forming a ball. At this stage, add 1 tbsp of ghee. Mix well till it stops sticking to the bottom and forms a non-sticky ball.

6. Turn off the flame and let it cool down a bit. Take it out on the greased work platform and knead it for 5 minutes to make the smooth burfi.

7. Put butter paper on a flat plate and spread the dough on it. Roll it by pressing with palm or roll it with the help of a rolling pin. Keep the thickness from 0.5 cm to 0.75 cm. Let it cool down.

8. Dry roast 10-15 almonds and open them in the vertical half.

9. Grease your palm with about ¼ tsp ghee and pat the top of the burfi. Cut in squares and stick half an almond on each piece. Keep in refrigerator and consume within 2 days.

Tips:

1. Make sure to steam sweet potatoes; do not boil them. Boiling makes sweet potato mushy and strong-flavored that disrupts the balanced taste of burfi.

2. The quantity of jaggery depends on the sweetness of the sweet potato. So adjust the jaggery quantity accordingly.

4

Eat for Maximum Health Benefits

(THE ULTIMATE NUTRIENT COMBINATIONS)

Nutrients need to be adequately absorbed into the body to provide health benefits. Some nutrients are rapidly eliminated from your body without being absorbed, and you don't get their health benefits. Various factors affect the absorption of nutrients. Foods require a favorable environment and the presence of specific vitamins and minerals inside the body to be absorbed. If the foods aren't absorbed into your body, you don't get the health benefits. Fortunately, you can increase the absorption of food by combining it with other foods that provide the necessary environment for their absorption and inhibit their metabolism. As a result, nutrients are more available to be absorbed into the bloodstream, and you get maximum health benefits from them.

Here are recipes of nutrient combinations that provide maximum health benefits when eaten together:

Ginger Green Iced Tea

Green tea + Lemon

Serves: 4
Prep time: 20 mins
Cooking time: 10 mins
Beverage

Ingredients

Green tea:	4 tsp/ 4 green tea bag
Mint leaves:	20
Lemon:	2 tbsp
Ice cubes:	12 (optional)
Basil leaves:	20
Ginger:	2 inches
Water:	1 L
Lemon slices:	For garnish
Honey:	To taste

Method

1. Crush ginger with a pestle. Add green tea, basil leaves, and ginger to the water. Bring it to a boil. Simmer for 5-7 minutes.
2. Add mint leaves and lemon juice and turn off the flame. Cover and leave for 15 minutes till tea reaches room temperature.
3. Strain the tea. Add honey if you want to sweeten your tea.
4. Chill the tea in the refrigerator for 3-4 hours.
5. Pour the chilled ginger green iced tea into glasses. Add lemon slices, basil leaves, and ice cubes. Enjoy this summer drink.

7 Anaj With Khunua

Phytic acid + Water

**Serves: 4 | Prep time: 10 mins
Cooking time: 15 mins
Breakfast**

Ingredients

Brown chickpeas:	50 g
Whole wheat:	80 g
Whole mung beans:	50 g
Peanuts:	50 g
Khunua:	1 tsp/as required
Salt:	To taste
Whole yellow peas:	50 g
Whole pigeon peas:	50 g
Soybean:	50 g
Water:	850 ml
Mustard oil:	1 tsp

Method

1. Soak all 7 anaj overnight in enough water.
2. Next morning wash all anaj with fresh water 4 to 5 times.
3. Put all 7 anaj in the pressure cooker. Add water and ½ tsp salt only as khunua already contains salt. Pressure cook for 5-7 whistles.
4. Open the lid. Add khunua and mustard oil. Mix well.
5. Start your day with the soupy 7 Anaj with the heavenly taste of raw garlic and mustard oil.

Mixed Sprouts

Vitamin C + Iron | Complete protein

Serves: 4 | Prep time: 15 mins | Breakfast/snack

Ingredients

Sprouted brown chickpeas:	75 g	Sprouted mung beans:	75 g
Sprouted horse gram:	50 g	Boiled corn kernels:	50 g
Sprouted fenugreek seeds:	20 g	Sprouted peanuts:	25 g
Apple:	2	Cucumber:	1
Pomegranate:	1	Tomato:	1
Onion:	1	Chopped green chilies:	To taste
Lemon juice:	1 tbsp	Kala namak mix:	To taste
Chopped mint leaves:	1 tbsp	Chopped coriander leaves:	1 tbsp

Method

1. Chop apple, cucumber, chilies, onion, and tomato.
2. Put all the ingredients of mixed sprouts in a bowl. Mix well.
3. Leave for 10 minutes. Enjoy fresh mixed sprouts.

Avoid green chilies if you have acidity or heartburn.

Easy-to-Digest Sprouts

Serves: 4 | Prep time: 5 mins
Cooking time: 10 mins
Breakfast

Ingredients

Sprouted brown chickpeas:	75 g
Sprouted mung beans:	75 g
Sprouted peanuts:	50 g
Black pepper powder:	¼ tsp
Asafoetida:	¼ tsp
Water:	75 ml
Sprouted whole pigeon peas:	50 g
Sprouted horse gram:	50 g
Cumin seeds:	1 tsp
Chopped green chilies:	To taste
Salt:	To taste
Mustard oil:	1 tsp

Method

1. Heat oil in a pressure cooker. Add asafoetida, green chilies, and cumin seeds. When cumin seeds start changing color, add all sprouts.

2. Cook for 5 minutes. Add black pepper powder, salt, and water.

3. Pressure cook for 2-3 whistles. Turn off the flame. Let the pressure release naturally. Enjoy the Easy-to-Digest Sprouts every morning.

Fruit Chaat

Vitamin D + Calcium | Folate + Vitamin B12

Serves: 4 | Prep time: 20 mins | Snack

Ingredients

Thick curd:	250 g	Apple:	2
Banana:	2	Pomegranate:	1
Orange:	1	Papaya:	50 g
Kiwi:	2	Musk melon:	50 g
Plus, any seasonal fruits		Almond:	10
Pistachios:	10	Walnut:	3 kernels
Pumpkin seeds:	3 tsp	Cumin seeds:	1 tsp
Chopped mint leaves:	2 tbsp	Honey:	1 tbsp
Kala namak mix:	To taste	Dry mango powder:	¼ tsp

Method

1. Dry roast cumin seeds till they change color. Coarsely grind them.
2. Smoothen the curd by blending it with a spoon for 2 minutes.
3. Chop all the ingredients. Add them in curd. Mix well.
4. Add cumin seeds, dry mango powder, kala namak mix, and honey to it. Mix well. Refrigerate for 1 hour. Serve chilled.

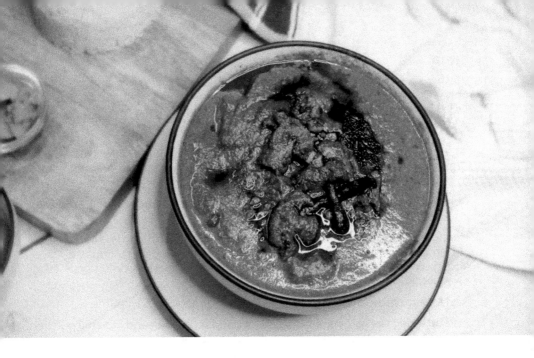

Mushroom in Creamy Spinach Gravy

Vitamin C + Iron | Vitamin D + Calcium | Folate + Vitamin B12

Serves: 4 | Prep time: 15 mins | Cooking time: 1 hour | Main course
(Weekend special)

Ingredients

Button mushrooms:	200 g		Spinach:	200 g
Cashew nuts:	30		Melon seeds:	20 g
Onion:	4 medium		Tomato:	3 medium
Ginger:	1 ½ inch		Garlic:	10 cloves
Turmeric powder:	¼ tsp		Garam masala:	1 tsp
Coriander powder:	½ tsp		Red chili powder:	½ tsp
Asafoetida:	¼ tsp		Bay leaf:	1
Cumin seeds:	½ tsp		Water:	250 ml
Lemon juice:	1 tsp		Salt:	To taste
Ghee:	2 tbsp			

For Tadka

Chopped garlic:	1 tbsp
Asafoetida:	¼ tsp
Kashmiri red chili powder:	½ tsp
Ghee:	1 tsp

Method

1. Wash spinach thoroughly. Discard the stems and use fresh spinach leaves only. Blanch the spinach in 100 ml of water with salt and lemon juice for 1 minute. Let it cool and blend to a smooth paste.

2. Soak cashew nuts and melon seeds in 100 ml of hot water for 15 minutes. Grind to a fine white paste.

3. Grind together onion, ginger, and garlic to a fine paste. Separately blend tomatoes without adding water.

4. Cut mushroom into 1-inch cubes. Heat ½ tsp of ghee. Add mushroom pieces and sauté for 10 minutes.

5. Heat ghee in another pan. Add asafoetida, bay leaf, and cumin seeds. When cumin seeds start changing color, add the onion-ginger-garlic paste. Cover and cook on low flame for 10 minutes till the raw taste of onion goes away completely.

6. Add tomato paste and salt. Mix well. Cover and cook for 5 minutes.

7. Add turmeric powder, garam masala, coriander powder, and red chili powder. Cover and cook on low flame for 10 minutes. Stir occasionally.

8. Add cashew-melon paste. Cover and cook on low flame for 15 minutes till the gravy leaves oil.

9. Add spinach paste and mix well. Bring it to a boil. If the gravy is too thick, add 50 to 100 ml water. Simmer for 5 minutes on low flame.

10. Add mushrooms. Mix and simmer for 2 minutes. Turn off the flame.

For Tadka

1. Add asafoetida, chopped garlic, and red chili powder to the hot ghee. Cook for 2-3 minutes.

2. Add tadka to mushroom in creamy spinach gravy. Cover and leave for 5 minutes. Serve with chapati and rice.

Winter Curry

Turmeric + Black pepper

Serves: 4
Prep time: 20 mins
Cooking time: 1 hour
Main course

Ingredients

Cauliflower:	250 g	Sweet potato:	100 g
Carrot:	100 g	Garlic:	8-10 cloves
Ginger:	2 inches	Onion:	3 medium
Tomato:	2 medium	Green chilies:	2
Turmeric powder:	½ tsp	Black pepper powder:	¼ tsp
Garam masala:	1 tsp	Coriander-cumin powder:	1 tsp
Red chili powder:	¼ tsp	Asafoetida:	½ tsp
Bay leaf:	1	Cumin seeds:	½ tsp
Fenugreek seeds powder:	¼ tsp	Salt:	To tatse
Mustard oil:	2½ tbsp	Water:	300 ml

Method

1. Peel sweet potato and carrot. Cut cauliflower, sweet potato, and carrot into one-inch cubes.

2. Grind together onion, ginger, garlic, and green chilies coarsely. Make sure not to make a fine paste. Grind tomatoes separately.

3. Heat 1 tsp of oil in a pan. Add ¼ tsp asafoetida and cauliflower. Cook on low flame for 10 minutes till brown spots appear on the cauliflower. Take out the cauliflower from the pan.

4. In the same pan, add ½ tsp oil. Add sweet potato pieces. Cook for 10 minutes until they slightly turn brown. Remove them from heat. Add ½ tsp oil and add carrot. Cook for 7-10 minutes. Remove them from heat.

5. Heat 1½ tbsp oil in the same pan. Add asafoetida, bay leaf, cumin seeds, and fenugreek seeds powder. Cook for 2 minutes.

6. Add onion-ginger-garlic paste. Cook for 10 minutes.

7. Add turmeric powder, black pepper powder, red chili powder, garam masala, coriander-cumin powder. Cook for 5 minutes on low flame.

8. Add tomato paste. Mix well. Cook for 5-7 minutes.

9. Add salt and 300 ml water. Add cauliflower, carrot, and sweet potato pieces. If you prefer more ras, add 50 ml-100 ml more water as per your taste. Do not add too much water as it will dilute the taste.

10. Cover with a lid and cook on low flame for 10 minutes.

11. Turn off the flame. Serve with chapati and rice.

Masala Mixed Dal

Vitamin C + Iron | Tomato + Olive oil | Phytic acid + Water

Serves: 4 | Prep time: 15 mins | Cooking time: 30 mins | Main course

Ingredients

Split yellow pigeon pea:	4 tbsp	Split green pigeon pea:	2 tbsp
Red lentils:	2 tbsp	Split yellow mung beans:	2 tbsp
Tomato:	1 medium	Salt:	To taste
Asafoetida:	½ tsp	Peanuts:	2 tbsp
Turmeric powder:	1 tsp	Coriander powder:	½ tsp
Garam masala:	1 tsp	Cumin seeds	½ tsp
Mustard seeds:	1 tsp	Dry red chilies:	2
Curry leaves:	5-6	Water:	700 ml
Kokum:	3	Olive oil:	1 tbsp

Method

1. Soak peanuts in hot water for 15 minutes.

2. Soak kokum in about 100 ml of hot water for 15 minutes.

3. Wash lentils with fresh water and soak in enough water for 15 minutes to reduce cooking time and to remove phytic acid.

4. Discard the water. Take split yellow pigeon pea, split green pigeon pea, red lentils, split yellow moong beans, salt, turmeric powder, asafoetida, and chopped tomatoes in a pressure cooker. Add 400 ml of water and pressure cook for 4 whistles. The dal should be mushy. Blend smooth with a hand blender.

5. Heat oil in a pan. Add asafoetida, red chilies, mustard seeds, and cumin seeds. When mustard seeds start crackling, add curry leaves. Cook for a minute. Add dal mix, soaked peanuts, and rest of the water.

6. Let the dal boil. Add salt, garam masala, coriander powder, and kokum along with water (in which it was soaked).

7. Cook the dal on a medium flame for 10 minutes till it becomes slightly thick. Stir occasionally.

8. Turn off the flame. Garnish with coriander leaves. Enjoy the Masala Mixed Dal with rice.

Kokum substitute: If kokum is unavailable, you can replace it with 1 tbsp of lemon juice. If using lemon juice, make sure to add it after turning off the flame, not while cooking.

5

Eat to Prevent and Control Diabetes

Diabetes is a chronic disease in which the body either does not produce insulin or does not use insulin effectively, resulting in high blood sugar levels.

Healthy diet plays an important role in preventing and managing diabetes. Controlling diabetes isn't just about avoiding foods that can increase your blood sugar levels. It is also about choosing the right foods which naturally prevent and control diabetes.

Healthy Alternatives to Prevent and Control Diabetes:

Replace Potatoes with Sweet Potatoes

Sweet potatoes have a sweeter taste than potatoes and give the false impression that they increase sugar levels much faster than potatoes. But this is not true. The glycemic index of sweet potatoes is lower than that of potatoes. This is because the carbohydrates present in sweet potatoes are different than in potatoes. Carbohydrates in potatoes are quickly broken down and converted into sugar, causing a sudden spike in blood sugar levels.

On the other hand, the carbohydrates present in sweet potatoes slowly convert to sugar. So, sugar releases into the blood slowly and does not cause a sudden spike in blood sugar levels. This makes sweet potatoes safe for diabetic people when consumed in moderation.

Replace Sugar with Dried Fruits

Using dried fruits in place of sugar is a healthy option for people with diabetes. Dried fruits are rich in fiber, antioxidants, and healthy monounsaturated fats. When consumed in moderation, dried fruits such as dates (2–3 a day), raisins (2 tbsp a day), and figs can be safely used to sweeten desserts. However, each person may be in a different stage of diabetes. Depending on your diabetic condition, your doctor can tell you exactly how many dried fruits you should eat in a day, so consult your doctor to find out the right amount for you. Dried fruits are being used as a substitute for sugar in the following recipes. If it is not suitable for you, replace it with artificial sweetener or do as suggested by your doctor.

The recipes in this chapter are based on superfoods that have therapeutic effects and help prevent and control diabetes through the following mechanism of actions:

- Foods that mimick the action of insulin: **Bitter gourd.**

- Foods that increase glucose-induced insulin release: **Fenugreek**.

- Foods that are high in dietary fiber: **Bottle gourd** and **fenugreek.**

- Foods that reduce the risk of insulin resistance: **Bottle gourd, chickpeas,** and **green peas.**

- Foods that increase glucose metabolism and enhance insulin sensitivity: **Bottle gourd, bitter gourd,** and **Indian gooseberry.**

- Zinc-rich foods: **Cashew nuts, sesame seeds, chickpeas,** and **oats.**

- Monounsaturated fats rich foods: **Olive oil** and **dry fruits.**

- Foods that increase fat-burning hormone adiponectin in the body: **Olive oil, chickpeas,** and **green peas.**

- Foods that reduce oxidative stress in the body and control diabetic complications: **Indian gooseberry.**

Instant Amla Pickle

Makes: 350 g
Prep time: 15 mins
Cooking time: 15 mins
Condiment

Ingredients

Indian gooseberry:	250 g
Kala namak mix:	1 tbsp
Mustard oil:	2 tbsp
Fresh turmeric:	100 g
Asafoetida:	½ tsp

Method

1. Stream whole Indian gooseberries. Let them cool completely. Remove seeds. Peel and grate fresh turmeric.

2. Take grated turmeric and Indian gooseberry pieces in a bowl.

3. Add asafoetida, kala namak mix and mustard oil. Mix well.

4. Cover the bowl with a muslin cloth. Keep it in the sunlight for a day. Take it inside in the evening.

5. Fill Instant Amla Pickle in an airtight glass container. Store it under refrigeration for up to 2 weeks.

Amla Chutney

Makes: 120 g
Prep time: 10 mins
Condiment

Ingredients

Indian gooseberry:	100 g
Garlic:	7-8 cloves
Kala namak mix:	1 tbsp
Green chili:	1
Coriander leaves:	25 g

Method

1. Remove seeds from Indian gooseberry.

2. Put all ingredients in a grinder jar. Add coriander leaves along with the stem, no need to remove the stem.

3. Grind the chutney coarsely without adding water.

4. Enjoy the tangy Amla Chutney as it is or with rice and dal.

White Radish Stuffed Palak Paratha

Serves: 4
Prep time: 30 mins
Cooking time: 20 mins
Breakfast

Ingredients

For Stuffing

White radish:	500 gm
Cumin seeds:	1 tsp
Green garlic:	50 g
Ginger:	1 inch
Asafoetida:	½ tsp
Coriander leaves:	50 g
Salt:	To taste

For Paratha

Whole wheat flour:	400 g
Spinach:	150 g
Salt:	To taste
Lemon juice:	1 tbsp
Olive oil:	1 tbsp + as required

Method

For Stuffing

1. Peel and grate white radish. Sprinkle salt over grated radish. Cover and keep aside for 15 minutes. Squeeze radish to remove as much water as you can. Keep the water for kneading.

2. Dry roast cumin seeds and crush them with a pestle.

3. Add cumin seeds, asafoetida, chopped ginger, green garlic, and chopped coriander leaves to radish. Mix well.

For Paratha

1. Blanch the spinach with lemon juice and salt for 1 to 2 minutes using minimal water. Make a fine paste.

2. Add spinach paste and oil to whole wheat flour. Knead to a regular dough using radish water (if required).

3. Take a medium-sized ball from the dough. Make a smooth crack-free ball using your palms. Flatten the dough on your palm with your fingers. Keep center part a little thicker and sides thinner.

4. Put a spoonful of radish stuffing in the center, seal the edges. Dip it in dry whole wheat flour, dust off the excess flour. Use a rolling pin to roll the dough into a circle.

5. Heat the tawa/griddle/skillet on medium-high flame. Place the paratha on the skillet. Cook for about a minute. Flip the paratha and spread 3-4 drops of oil. Cook until it turns light brown.

6. Flip the paratha again and pour 3-4 drops of olive oil on top, and spread it evenly over the surface. Gently press the paratha with the flat spatula to help the paratha cook evenly.

7. When brown spots appear on both sides of the paratha, take out the paratha on a serving plate. Similarly, make all the parathas.

Multigrain Methi Puri

Makes: 165 g | Prep time: 30 mins | Cooking time: 15 mins | Snack

Ingredients

Oat Flour:	75 g	Whole wheat flour:	75 g
Semolina:	15 g	Turmeric powder:	1 tsp
Asafoetida:	A pinch	Salt:	To taste
Extra virgin olive oil:	1 tbsp	Garam masala:	1 tbsp

To Grind Together

Peanuts:	70 g	Onion:	2 medium
Ginger:	1 inch	Sprouted fenugreek seeds:	2 tbsp
Cloves:	5	Green chilies:	2
Fennel:	1 tbsp	White sesame seeds:	2 tbsp
Curd:	1 tbsp, if required	Lemon juice:	1½ tbsp

Method

1. Dry roast peanuts. Remove from heat. Once cool enough to handle, rub the peanuts between your palms to remove the skin.
2. Grind together peanuts, onion, ginger, cloves, chilies, fennel, sesame, sprouted fenugreek seeds, and lemon juice.
3. Take all three flours in a bowl. Add asafoetida, oil, salt, turmeric powder, garam masala, and mix well.
4. Add the prepared white paste to the flour mix and knead to make a slightly stiff dough. If the dough seems too dry, then add curd.
5. Pinch a medium-sized ball from the dough. Roll to a big round puri of thickness around 3 mm. Meanwhile, pre-heat the oven to 180 °C.
6. Take a fork and prick the surface of the puri so that it does not puff up while baking.
7. Take a cookie cutter and cut the puris into the desired shape. Repeat the same process for the rest of the dough.
8. Place the puris in a greased baking tray. Brush the puri top with oil. Bake puris in a pre-heated oven at 180 °C for 10 minutes. Flip the puris and bake for 5 minutes.

Tip: If you don't have sprouted fenugreek seeds available, use overnight soaked fenugreek seeds and add 1½ tbsp instead of 2 tbsp.

Almond Crackers

Makes: 150 g | Prep time: 15 mins | Cooking time: 15 mins | Snack

Ingredients

Whole wheat flour	100 g
Almond:	45 g
Salt:	1 tsp/to taste
Oats flour:	50 g
Desiccated coconut:	25 g
Water:	75-100 ml

For Topping

White sesame seeds:	1 tbsp
Desiccated coconut:	1 tbsp
Almond powder:	1 tbsp

Method

1. Dry roast almonds till they slightly change color. Cool and grind to make a fine powder. Save 1 tbsp of almond powder for the topping and use the rest for dough.

2. Take whole wheat flour, oat flour, desiccated coconut, almond powder, and salt in a bowl. Gradually add water and knead to a stiff dough. The dough should not be soft. Leave covered for 10 minutes.

3. Pinch medium size ball from the dough. Sprinkle flour to your work surface and roll the dough using a rolling pin. Keep the thickness to 3 mm to 4 mm.

4. Cut out the sides with a cutter to make large rectangular dough sheet.

5. Take a fork and prick it into the rolled dough so that the crackers do not puff up while baking.

6. Sprinkle sesame seeds, almond powder, and desiccated coconut over dough sheet. Tap with your fingers or roll gently with a rolling pin so that the nuts and seeds stick to the dough firmly.

7. With a zig-zag cutter or regular knife, cut the dough sheet to make 1 inch or 2 inches crackers.

8. Placed the crackers on the baking tray and bake in a pre-heated oven at 180 °C for 10 minutes. Flip the crackers and bake for 5 minutes or until the edges are browned.

9. Take out the crackers from the oven and allow them to cool completely before filling them in a container; otherwise, the crackers will lose their crunchiness.

10. Store in an airtight container and consume within 5 days.

Pyaz wale Karele

Serves: 4 | Prep time: 15 mins | Cooking time: 30 mins | Side dish

Ingredients

Bitter gourd:	250 g	Onion:	200 g
Dry mango powder:	½ tsp	Cumin seeds:	½ tsp
Panch phoran masala:	1 tsp	Asafoetida:	¼ tsp
Salt:	To taste	Oil:	2 tbsp

Method

1. Wash bitter gourd and soak them in salted hot water for 15 minutes to reduce their bitterness. Dry them thoroughly with a kitchen towel. Remove both ends and peel them but do not throw the peel (see tip).

2. Slice the bitter gourd and cut onion lengthwise.

3. Heat oil in a pan. Add asafoetida and cumin seeds. Cook for a minute. Add bitter gourds and cook on low flame for 15 minutes or till they become crispy. Add onions and cook for 10 minutes.

4. Add panch phoran masala, dry mango powder and salt. Cook for 5 minutes. Serve hot.

Tip: Take the peel of bitter gourd in a muslin cloth. Squeeze to collect bitter gourd juice. Discard the solid part and drink the juice while it is fresh. The juice will thicken if you keep it for later.

Mung Litti Chokha

Serves: 4 | Prep time: 30 mins | Cooking time: 50 mins | Main course (Weekend special)

Ingredients

For Dough

Whole wheat flour:	500 g
Water:	To knead
Salt:	To taste
Oil:	1 tbsp

For Chokha

Sweet potato:	150 g
Garlic:	8
Chopped coriander:	2 tbsp
Tomato:	3 medium
Chopped green chilies:	1
Salt:	To taste

For Mung Stuffing

Mung beans:	300 g
Turmeric powder:	½ tsp
Dry red chilies:	2
Salt:	To taste
Oil:	1 tsp
Cumin seeds:	1 tsp
Black pepper powder:	¼ tsp
Asafoetida:	½ tsp
Water:	200 ml

Method

For Dough

1. Take all ingredients except water in a bowl. Gradually add water and knead to a soft dough. Cover and leave aside for 30 minutes.

For Mung Stuffing

1. Soak mung beans in enough water overnight. Wash the overnight soaked mung beans with fresh water.

2. Heat oil in a pressure cooker. Add asafoetida, cumin seeds, and dry red chilies. Cook till cumin seeds change color.

3. Add mung beans. Cook for 5 minutes. Add turmeric powder, black pepper powder, and salt. Cook for 5 minutes.

4. Add water and pressure cook for 4 whistles on low flame. Mung beans should be completely cooked.

5. Mash the mung beans well with a masher or a pestle.

6. Return the cooker to heat and cook on low flame until all water evaporates and the stuffing dries up. Keep stirring it continuously to prevent the stuffing from sticking to the bottom of the cooker.

For Mung Litti

1. Take a medium-sized ball from the dough. Flatten the dough on your palm with your fingers. Keep center part a little thick and sides thin.

2. Fill a spoonful of mung stuffing in the center and seal the sides and make a ball. Gently press and flatten the litti.

3. Brush the littis with oil. Steam the littis in a steamer for 15 minutes.

4. Or bake the littis in a pre-heated oven at 200 °C for 10 minutes. Flip the littis and bake for 10-15 minutes.

For Chokha

1. Steam the sweet potatoes. Place the tomatoes and steamed sweet potatoes on a metal rack on a stove-top over direct flame. Roast from all sides till tomatoes are tender. Remove from heat.

2. Remove tomato and sweet potato skin and mash them.

3. Add crushed garlic, salt, chopped green chilies, and coriander leaves. Mix well and serve with Mung Littti.

Methi Matar in White Gravy

Serves: 4 | Prep time: 30 mins | Cooking time: 50 mins | Main course (Weekend Special)

Ingredients

Fresh fenugreek leaves:	200 g		Green peas:	100 g
Onion:	4 medium		Ginger:	1 inch
			Green chilies:	2-3
Garlic:	10		Cashew nuts:	50 g
Fresh curd:	200 g		Cumin seeds:	½ tsp
Melon seeds:	2 tbsp		Asafoetida:	¼ tsp
Bay leaf:	1		Coriander powder:	½ tsp
Garam masala:	1 tsp		Water:	200 ml + as required
Salt:	To taste			
Ghee:	1½ tbsp			

Method

1. Chop fenugreek leaves. Sprinkle salt, cover, and leave for 15 minutes. Fenugreek leaves will release water. Squeeze out all the water. This step will reduce the bitterness of fenugreek leaves. Do not throw fenugreek water. Use it for kneading dough.

2. Grind onion, ginger, garlic, and green chilies together to a fine paste.

3. Soak cashew nuts and melon seeds in 100 ml hot water for 15 minutes. Blend with water into a fine white paste.

4. Boil green peas in salted water for 5 minutes. Strain and discard the water. Keep green peas for later use.

5. Heat 1 tsp of ghee. Add fenugreek leaves. Cook for 8-10 minutes.

6. Meanwhile, heat 1 tbsp of ghee in another pan. Add asafoetida, cumin seeds, and bay leaf. Cook for a minute.

7. Add onion paste. Cover and cook for 15 minutes on low flame.

8. Add cashew-melon paste. Cover and cook for 15 minutes on low flame. Stir occasionally.

9. Beat the curd with a spatula until smooth. Keep the flame low. Add curd. Cook for 5 minutes.

10. Add garam masala, coriander powder, and salt. Mix well. Cover and cook on low flame for 10 minutes or till the gravy leave oil. You will see the oil on top of the gravy.

11. Add 150 ml water (add more water if required). Bring it to a boil. Turn the flame to low and add fenugreek leave and green peas. Mix well. Simmer for 5 minutes on low flame. Serve hot with chapati and rice.

Tips:

1. Use only fresh curd; otherwise, the gravy will turn sour. Another way to reduce the sourness of curd is to cook it well. The longer you cook the curd, the less sour it will be.

2. Always cook curd on low flame. Cooking on high flame may curdle the curd.

3. Adjust the amount of water according to taste. Gravy thickens with time. If your gravy has become thick, then add 50 ml-100 ml hot water and bring it to a boil.

Karela Kalonji

Serves: 4
Prep time: 30 mins
Cooking time: 30 mins
Main course
(Weekend special)

Ingredients

Bitter gourd:	10 small
Mustard oil:	1½ tbsp
Salt:	To taste

For Stuffing

Garlic:	1 whole bulb (22-25 cloves)
Panch phoran masala:	1 tbsp
Dry mango powder:	¼ tsp
Mustard oil:	1 tbsp
Onion:	5 medium
Ginger:	1 inch
Red chili powder:	¼ tsp
Salt:	To taste

Method

For Stuffing

1. Finely chop the onion, ginger and garlic.
2. Heat a tablespoon of oil in a pan. Add chopped ginger and garlic. Cook for 2 minutes.
3. Add chopped onion. Cook for 10-15 minutes on low flame till all onion moisture evaporates and onion dries up.
4. Add panch phoran, salt, red chili powder, and dry mango powder. Cook for 5 minutes. Keep aside.

For Karela Kalonji

1. Wash bitter gourd thoroughly and soak in hot and salted water for 15 minutes. Pat dry with a kitchen towel. Peel them.
2. Make vertical cuts. Carefully remove seeds with a small spoon to make an empty pocket. Fill a spoonful of onion masala in bitter gourd.
3. Steam the stuffed bitter gourds for 5-7 minutes, not more than that. This step is very important as it reduces 80% of the oil absorption of bitter gourds.
4. Heat a tablespoon of oil in a pan. Add 6-7 stuffed bitter gourds. Cover and cook for 15 minutes. Turn the bitter gourd every 3-4 minutes for even cooking. Cook till they are brown.
5. Once cooked, take out the bitter gourds from the pan. Add a teaspoon of oil and cook the rest of the stuffed bitter gourds.
6. Enjoy Karela Kaloji with chapati along with rice and dal in the afternoon on holiday, and you will not feel hungry till evening.

Tip: Cook the onion masala on low flame only. This may take longer, but it is an important step. Cooking the masala on low flame for a long time increases its sweetness and also enhances the taste.

Non-Fried Oats Bhature

Serves 4
Prep time: 10 mins
Cooking time: 20 mins
Main course

Ingredients

Oat flour:	300 g	Whole wheat flour:	200 g
Salt:	To taste	Baking powder:	½ tsp
Curd:	250 g/as required	Olive oil:	1 tbsp + as required

Method

1. Take oat flour and whole wheat flour in a large bowl. Add salt, baking powder, and oil. Mix well.

2. Gradually add curd and knead for 5-6 minutes. The dough should be a little stiff for making crispy bhature. Add more curd if required.

3. Cover the dough with a wet muslin cloth. Leave it for 3 hours.

4. Grease your palm well with oil. Take a medium size ball of dough and make a ball shape between your palms. Smooth out the ball, make sure it is crack-free. Roll it into oval shape or round disc.

5. Heat a Tawa/skillet. Grease it with oil and put bhatura on it.

6. First, cook from one side. Spread ½ tsp of oil on top surface of bhatura. Turn and cook the other side. When brown spots appear on both sides, it's done. Eat Non-Fried Oats Bhature with chole masala.

Chole Masala

Serves 4 | Prep time: 15 mins
Cooking time: 50 mins
Main course
(Weekend special)

Ingredients

Uncooked dried Chickpeas:	400 g
Onion:	1 medium
Water:	1200 ml
Tea bags:	4
Salt:	To taste

For Gravy

Garlic:	1 bulb/25-28 cloves	Ginger:	2 inches
		Asafoetida:	1 tsp
Onion:	6 medium	Bay leaves:	2
Cumin seeds:	1 tsp	Turmeric powder:	½ tsp
Red chili powder:	½ tsp	Garam masala:	1 tsp
Chole masala:	2 tbsp	Dry mango powder:	1 tsp
Water:	300 ml		
Mustard oil:	2 tbsp	Salt:	To taste

Method

1. Soak the chickpeas in enough water overnight or for at least 8 hours.

2. Next day, drain the water and rinse chickpeas thoroughly.

3. Take the soaked chickpeas, tea bags, salt, sliced onion (1 medium), and 1200 ml water in a pressure cooker. Pressure cook on medium flame for 5-6 whistles. It will take around 15 minutes. The chickpeas should be soft when you mash them with a spoon. If chickpeas are hard, then pressure cook them for two whistles.

4. Squeeze and discard the tea bags. Strain the chickpeas and keep the stock for later use.

5. Grind onion, garlic, and ginger together to make a smooth paste.

6. Add mustard oil to the hot pan. Add asafoetida, cumin seeds, and bay leaves, and sauté for 2 minutes.

7. Add the onion paste to the oil. Mix well and cover the pan with a lid. Cook on medium-low flame for 15 minutes. Cook till it leaves oil.

8. Add chole masala, garam masala, turmeric powder, dry mango powder, red chili powder, and salt. Cook for 5 minutes.

9. Add chickpeas and mix well. Masala mixture should coat the chickpeas entirely. Cook for 5-7 minutes.

10. Add the chickpeas stock plus 300 ml of water. Don't add too much water as it will dilute the taste.

11. Bring it to a boil. Turn the flame to low. Cook for 10 minutes until chickpeas absorb the flavor of masala. The gravy should be thick.

12. Your Chole Masala is ready to eat. Eat it with non-fried oats bhature or brown rice.

Anjeer Kaju Katli

Zinc deficiency may lead to the development of diabetes. Zinc plays an important role in preventing and managing diabetes. It is because zinc plays a crucial part in the production and secretion of insulin. Since zinc strengthens the immune system, it protects beta cells from destruction. Studies suggest that zinc-rich foods help lower blood sugar levels in type 1 as well as type 2 diabetes. Cashew nuts are a great source of zinc. This sweet dish is all about cashew nuts and requires less sweetness as compared to other sweets. The milder the sweetness, the richer cashew nuts will taste.

Makes: 200 g | Prep time: 20 mins | Cooking time: 15 mins | Dessert

Ingredients

Cashew nuts:	200 g	Dried figs:	22
Water:	180 ml	Ghee:	For greasing
Edible silver leaves/ vark:	3 or 4		

Method

1. Wash figs thoroughly and soak them in 180 ml water for 2 hours.

2. Take figs along with water in a pressure cooker. Pressure cook for 3-4 whistles. Turn off the flame. Let it cool down. Blend it in a blender to make a fine paste. Make sure the paste is smooth.

3. Take the paste in a muslin cloth. Squeeze to collect the smooth fig paste. Discard the solid part. Alternatively, you can pass it through a sieve and discard the solid part.

4. Finely grind cashew nuts. Pass through a sieve and grind the coarse nuts again to make a fine powder.

5. Take the fig paste in a pan. Bring it to a boil. Cook till it reduces to one-fourth of the volume and the water has almost evaporated.

6. When the fig paste starts separating from the pan, add cashew powder. Mix well and keep stirring continuously so that it does not stick to the bottom of the pan. Keep the flame medium.

7. Cook till mixture comes together and releases oil. You will notice oil around the mixture, and it will start separating from the pan. It takes around 3-5 minutes to reach this stage. Turn off the flame.

8. Take out the mixture in a well-greased bowl or plate. Let it cool down for 5 minutes. It will dry out and look like dough.

9. Knead the anjeer kaju katli dough for 3 minutes.

10. Place the dough on butter paper, place another butter paper over it, and flatten the dough into a thickness of 3 to 5 mm with a rolling pin.

11. Remove the butter paper from the top. Apply silver vark while the kaju katli is still hot. If the anjeer kaju katli has become cold, then grease it with ghee and apply the silver vark. Cut in diamond or square shape. Keep the Anjeer Kaju Katli in the refrigerator and consume it within 3 days.

1. Do not grind cashews at high speed or for a long time, or else it will start releasing oil which is not good for this recipe.

2. Do not add extra water than what is mentioned in the recipe. The fig paste may seem thick and less initially, but it is enough to make the perfect anjeer kaju katli. If you add more water, katli will become sticky and will not dry out later and look like halwa.

3. Applying silver vark is optional. Traditionally Kaju Katli has silver vark, but it is completely optional. Make sure to check the product label. It should clearly specify that it's 100% vegetarian or confirm with the seller if the silver vark is 100% vegetarian. When in doubt, omit silver vark completely.

Lauki ki Kheer

Serve: 4 | Prep time: 20 mins
Cooking time: 40 mins
Dessert

Ingredients

Bottle gourd:	200 g
Dates:	11-13
Raisins:	10
Ghee:	1 tbsp
Milk:	1 L
Almonds:	8
Cashew nuts:	8
Saffron:	5-6 strands

Method

1. Soak saffron in 2 tbsp of hot milk. Keep aside. Remove seeds from dates. Blend with 50 ml of milk to make a smooth paste. Keep aside.

2. Peel and grate bottle gourd (remove seeds). Heat ghee in a pan. Add the grated bottle gourd and cook for 5-8 minutes. Bottle gourd should be cooked well, or it might curdle the milk.

3. Meanwhile, bring milk to a boil in another pan. Cook on medium flame till the milk thickens slightly. Stir occasionally.

4. Add cooked bottle gourd. Cook for 20-25 minutes on medium flame.

5. Add date paste, saffron milk, chopped almond, chopped cashew nuts, and raisins. The kheer will start thickening immediately. Simmer for 5 minutes on low flame.

6. Turn off the flame. Allow the kheer to cool to room temperature, then refrigerate for 2-3 hours. Enjoy chilled Lauki ki Kheer.

6
Eat to Prevent and
Control Hypertension

Blood pressure is the measure of the force of blood against blood vessel walls. The blood pressure increases when the force of blood against the artery walls is too high, and this condition is known as hypertension or high blood pressure. To prevent and control hypertension, your diet should be rich in foods that have the following therapeutic effects:

· Foods that have diuretics effects.

· Foods that have potent vasodilating properties.

· Foods rich in magnesium as magnesium is a natural calcium channel blocker.

· Foods rich in potassium because potassium negates the sodium effect.

· Foods that keep nitric oxide levels high in your body.

Superfoods that prevent and control hypertension are:

Vasodilator: **Beetroot** and **garlic.**

Diuretics: **Cucumber** and **lemon.**

Magnesium-rich foods: **Spinach, kidney beans, pumpkin seeds, pistachios,** and **sweet potato.**

Potassium-rich foods: **Cucumber, sweet potato, kidney beans, banana, spinach,** and **curd.**

Foods that increase nitric oxide production in the body: **Beetroot, honey,** and **pumpkin seeds.**

This chapter helps you include superfoods in your diet that help prevent and manage hypertension effectively.

Cucumber Jaljeera

Serves: 4 | Prep time: 15 mins | Cooking time: 5 mins | Beverage

Ingredients

Lemon juice:	2 tbsp		Mint leaves:	50 g
Coriander leaves:	30 g		Ginger:	1½ inches
Green chili:	1		Cumin seeds:	1 tsp
Dried mango powder:	½ tsp		Asafoetida:	½ tsp
Black salt:	To taste		Black pepper:	10
Cloves:	4		Cucumber pieces:	4 tbsp
Water:	1 L			

Method

1. Dry roast cumin seeds, cloves, and black pepper till cumin seeds turn reddish-brown. Cool and grind them.
2. Finely chop the cucumber. Keep aside for later.
3. Take all the ingredients in the blender jar except the cucumber. Add about 50 ml - 100 ml of water and grind to make a super-fine paste.
4. Take the green paste in a jar and add more water to make 1 L. Add cucumber pieces. Refrigerate it for 2 hours. Serve chilled.

Summer Fruit Punch

Serves: 4 | Prep time: 15 mins
Beverage

Ingredients

Musk melon:	500 g
Orange:	200 g
Honey:	1 tbsp/To taste
Dry mango powder:	1 tsp
Cucumber:	250 g
Mint leaves:	50 g
Lemon juice:	1 tbsp
Ice cubes:	8-10 (optional)

Method

1. Chill musk melon, cucumber, orange, and mint leaves in the refrigerator for 3-4 hours.

2. Keep 4-5 mint leaves to garnish. Blend musk melon, cucumber, orange and mint leaves, lemon juice, and honey in a blender.

3. Pour the fruit punch into glasses. Sprinkle dry mango powder over it. If you want, put 2-3 ice cubes in each glass. Enjoy the chilled and refreshing Summer Fruit Punch.

Banana Choco Milk Shake

Serves: 4 | Prep time: 15 mins | Beverage

Ingredients

Banana:	4
Cocoa powder:	1 tbsp
Pistachios:	2 tbsp
Chilled cow milk:	800 ml
Honey:	1 tbsp (optional)
Pumpkin seeds:	1 tbsp

Method

1. Dry roast pistachios and pumpkin seeds till they start releasing an aromatic smell and turn slightly brown. Remove from flame and let the nuts cool down. Chop them roughly using a knife or crush them using the mortar pestle or grinder.

2. Chop banana roughly. Blend banana, cocoa powder, and chilled milk into a smooth milkshake. Pour into glasses and add honey if needed.

3. Add pistachios and pumpkin seeds. Mix well and serve.

Crispi Garlici Sweet Potato

Serves: 4 | Prep time: 15 mins | Cooking time: 20 mins | Snack

Ingredients

Sweet potato:	600 g	Rock salt:	To taste
Kashmiri red chili powder:	1 tbsp	Black pepper powder:	1 tsp
Garlic:	15-18 cloves	Oil:	2½ tbsp
Corn flour:	1 tbsp	Dry mango powder:	½ tsp

Method

1. Wash sweet potatoes thoroughly. Peel them or leave the skin on. Cut them with a zig-zag knife or simple knife to medium thickness.

2. Steam sweet potatoes in a steamer for 5 minutes, not more than that.

3. Crush garlic finely using mortar pestle. Add Kashmiri red chili powder, salt, black pepper powder, and oil. Mix well.

4. Take out sweet potatoes in a colander. Add corn flour and toss to coat sweet potatoes evenly.

5. Add the garlic seasoning. Toss until sweet potatoes are evenly coated with the seasoning and don't look dry.

6. Divide sweet potatoes into 2 batches. Place one batch on a greased baking dish. Make sure they do not overlap each other.

7. If you have the grill function in your oven, grill sweet potatoes for 12 minutes. Flip the sides and grill again for 3-5 minutes.

8. Alternatively, bake the sweet potatoes in a pre-heated oven at 200 °C for 15 minutes. Flip the sides for even cooking and bake for 5-10 minutes or until sweet potatoes are crisp and browned from corners.

9. Take them out from the oven. Sprinkle dry mango powder and enjoy Crispi Garlici Sweet Potato with bell pepper chutney.

Tip: Steaming sweet potatoes shortens the baking time and prevents the sweet potatoes from releasing sugar. Cooking in this way makes sweet potatoes even more healthy.

Multigrain Beetroot Paratha

Serves: 4
Prep time: 15 mins
Cooking time: 20 mins
Breakfast

Ingredients

Grated beetroot:	150 g
Whole wheat flour:	150 g
Gram flour/ chickpea flour:	75 g
Amaranth flour:	25 g
Ginger garlic paste:	1 tbsp
Jaggery:	1 tbsp
Garam masala:	1½ tsp
Asafoetida:	a pinch
Crushed fenugreek seeds:	1 tsp
Curd:	2 tbsp (to knead)
Grated bottle gourd:	150 g
Oat flour:	150 g
Salt:	To taste
Coriander powder:	1 tsp
Red chili powder:	1 tsp
Turmeric:	½ tsp
Sesame seeds:	1½ tbsp
Olive oil:	1 tbsp+ as needed

Method

1. Take all ingredients along with one tbsp of olive oil in a bowl.

2. Gradually add curd and knead to a stiff dough.

3. Take a dough ball, dip it in the dry whole wheat flour, and dust off the excess flour. Use a rolling pin to roll the dough into a circle.

4. Heat the pan/griddle/skillet (Tawa) on medium-high flame.

5. Place the paratha on the skillet. Cook for about a minute or cook until the paratha begins puffing up from the base at some places.

6. Flip the paratha and spread 3-4 drops of olive oil. Cook for 2 minutes until it turns light brown.

7. Flip the paratha again and top with 3-4 drops of olive oil, spread it evenly over the surface. Press the paratha gently with a flat spatula so that the paratha gets cooked evenly.

8. Once you begin to see brown spots on both sides of the paratha, transfer the paratha to a serving plate. Your paratha is ready. Similarly, make all the parathas.

9. Enjoy Multigrain Beetroot Paratha with mixed veg raita.

Mixed Veg Raita

Serves: 4 | Prep time: 15 mins | Side dish

Ingredients

Curd:	400 g	Grated beetroot:	2 tbsp
Finely chopped onion:	50 g	Finely chopped tomato:	50 g
Finely chopped cabbage:	50 g	Finely chopped cucumber:	50 g
Brown sugar:	1 tbsp	Kala namak mix:	1 tsp/to taste
Cumin seeds powder:	1 tbsp	Red chili powder:	½ tsp

Method

1. Blend the curd until smooth. Mix all veggies except beetroot in it.
2. Add kala namak mix, brown sugar, red chili powder, and cumin seeds powder to the curd. Mix well.
3. Keep the raita in the refrigerator for half an hour.
4. Garnish with grated beetroot. Enjoy Mixed Veg Raita with multigrain beetroot paratha.

Cucumber Salad

Serves: 4 | Prep time: 15 mins | Salad

Ingredients

Cucumber:	1 large		Banana:	1
Sprouted brown chickpeas:	3 tbsp		Pomegranate:	3 tbsp
			Red chili powder:	½ tsp
Peanuts:	2 tbsp		Lemon juice:	2 tbsp
Honey:	1 tsp		Kala namak mix:	To taste
Chopped mint leaves:	2 tbsp			
Coriander leaves:	2 tbsp			

Method

1. Soak peanuts in water for 2 hours.
2. Cut banana and cucumber into half-inch cubes.
3. Roughly chop mint leaves and coriander leaves.
4. Take all ingredients in a bowl and mix well. Cover and leave for 15 minutes until the lemon juice moistens the salad. Enjoy the Cucumber Salad.

Rajma

Serves: 4 | Prep time: 15 mins
Cooking time: 30 mins | Main course
(Weekend special)

Ingredients

Kidney beans:	300 g
Tomato:	4 medium
Chopped garlic:	1 tbsp
Bay leaf:	1
Garam masala:	1½ tbsp
Turmeric powder:	½ tsp
Salt:	To taste
Water:	900 ml
Onion:	4 medium (1+3)
Chopped ginger:	1 tbsp
Asafoetida:	1 tsp
Cumin seeds:	½ tsp
Coriander powder:	1 tsp
Red chili powder:	1 tsp
Mustard oil:	2 tbsp
Coriander leaves:	20 g

Method

1. Soak kidney beans in enough water overnight.

2. Cut onion lengthwise. Keep one onion for cooking kidney beans and the rest three for gravy.

3. Pressure cook kidney beans with one onion, salt, and water for 3-4 whistle. Check whether the kidney beans are cooked; If not, pressure cook for 2 more whistles.

4. Strain the cooked kidney beans and keep the stock for gravy.

5. Heat mustard oil in a pan. Once the oil is hot, add bay leaf, asafoetida, and cumin seeds.

6. When cumin seeds start changing color, add ginger and garlic and cook on medium flame for 2 minutes.

7. Add onions and cook for 6-8 minutes till onions turn translucent.

8. Add chopped tomatoes and salt. Mix well and cover with a lid and cook on low flame for 10 minutes. Stir occasionally.

9. Add garam masala, coriander powder, red chili powder, turmeric powder, and mix well. Cover and cook on low flame for 5 minutes.

10. Add kidney beans and cook for 5 minutes on medium flame.

11. Add stock and bring it to a boil. Pressure cook for 1-2 whistles.

12. Garnish with coriander leaves and enjoy Rajma with rice and chapati.

Mixed Veg Pulao

Serves: 4 | Prep time: 15 mins
Cooking time: 30 mins | Main course
(Weekend special)

Ingredients

Basmati rice:	400 g
Cabbage:	150 g
Cloves:	6
Cinnamon:	1 inch
Cumin seeds:	1 tsp
Bay leaf:	1
Ghee:	2 tbsp
Peas:	150 g
Carrot:	150 g
Black pepper:	10
Green cardamom:	3
Asafoetida:	½ tsp
Salt:	To taste
Water:	850 ml

Method

1. Wash rice in running water and soak rice for 15 minutes.
2. Chop cabbage and carrot.
3. Crush clove, cardamom, cinnamon, and black pepper in a mortar with the help of a pestle.
4. Heat ghee in a pressure cooker. Add bay leaf, asafoetida, cumin seeds, crushed cloves, cinnamon, cardamom, and black pepper. Cook till cumin seeds start changing color.
5. Add peas and salt, cover with a lid, and cook for 5 minutes till peas are tender.
6. Add carrots and cook for 5 minutes without covering. Add cabbage and cook for 5 minutes without covering.
7. Strain the rice and add it to the vegetable mixture. Cook for 6-8 minutes. Stir occasionally to prevent rice from sticking at the bottom of the cooker. Do not stir vigorously; otherwise, the rice will break.
8. Add water and close the lid of the cooker. Cook on medium flame for 1 whistle. Turn off the flame. Leave for 5 minutes and open the lid. Do not keep the lid of the pressure cooker on for a long time; otherwise, the rice will be soggy.
9. Enjoy Mixed Veg Pulav as it is or with rajma or dal fry.

Dal Fry Palak Wale

Serves: 4 | Prep time: 20 mins
Cooking time: 40 mins | Main course

Ingredients

Spinach:	200 g
Split Bengal gram:	50 g
Water:	650 ml
Yellow split pigeon peas:	140 g
Salt:	To taste
Turmeric:	½ tsp

For Tadka

Ginger:	1 inch
Onion:	1 medium
Garam masala:	½ tsp
Red chili powder:	¼ tsp
Asafoetida:	½ tsp
Water:	250 ml
Garlic:	6 cloves
Tomatoes:	1 medium
Coriander powder:	½ tsp
Cumin seeds:	½ tsp
Oil:	1 tbsp

Method

1. Wash and chop the spinach leaves. Wash split pigeon peas and split Bengal gram 2-3 times and soak them in water for 15 minutes.

2. Discard the water. Take dal in the pressure cooker, add fresh 650 ml water. Bring it to a boil. Add salt, turmeric powder, and spinach leaves. Close the lid and pressure cook on a medium flame for 4 whistles.

3. Heat oil in a pan. Add asafoetida and cumin seeds. Cook till cumin seeds start changing color.

4. Add chopped ginger and garlic and cook for 2 minutes. Add onion and cook for 5-7 minutes. Add tomato. Cook for 5 minutes.

5. Add garam masala, coriander powder, and red chili powder. Mix well. Cover and cook for 10 minutes. Mash the mix with a spatula.

6. Add dal to it and mix. Add 250 ml water, if required, add more water. Bring it to a boil. Cook on low flame for 5-10 minutes. Serve hot with rice.

Note: Spinach absorbs less salt, due to which you will need less salt than usual, so add salt accordingly.

Chocolate Shrikhand

Serves: 4 | Prep time: 12 hours | Dessert

Ingredients

Fresh thick curd:	2 L	Cocoa powder:	2 tbsp
Honey:	To taste	Vanilla essence:	½ tsp
Dark chocolate pieces:	4 tbsp	Dark chocolate shaves:	2 tbsp

Method

1. Tie thick curd in a muslin cloth and hang it in a tap or any other place overnight or for 6-7 hours.

2. Take out the hung curd in a bowl. Blend it with a spoon or hand blender to make it smooth.

3. Mix cocoa powder, honey, and vanilla essence in the hung curd.

4. Take shrikhand in a muslin cloth and pass the shrikhand through muslin cloth by squeezing the muslin cloth. Alternatively, pass the shrikhand through a sieve to make it smooth.

5. Add the chocolate pieces and mix well. Refrigerate it for 3-4 hours.

6. Take out Shrikhand in individual serving bowls. Decorate with chocolate shavings. Keep the bowl in the refrigerator for half an hour and enjoy Chocolate Shrikhand after lunch.

Red Velvet Halwa

Serves: 4 | Prep time: 10 mins | Cooking time: 30 mins | Dessert

Ingredients

Grated Beetroot:	300 g	Milk:	500 ml
Jaggery:	50 g	Desiccated coconut:	6 tbsp
Chopped mixed nuts:	2 tbsp	Ghee:	½ tsp

Method

1. Heat ghee in a pan. Add chopped nuts and roast till they start releasing a pleasant aromatic smell. Make sure to stir continuously; otherwise, nuts will burn. Take out the nuts and keep them aside.

2. In the same pan, add milk and bring it to a boil. Keep boiling till the milk thickens slightly (about 5-7 minutes on high flame).

3. Add grated beetroot to the milk. Keep the flame medium-high and let it cook till all milk evaporates. Keep stirring it to prevent it from sticking to the bottom of the pan. It will take about 15 to 20 minutes.

4. When the milk has reduced to about 90%, it will look like a slurry. Add jaggery and desiccated coconut at this stage.

5. Cook for 5 minutes till the beetroot absorbs all the milk and starts leaving the pan. Turn off the flame. Add all nuts and mix well.

6. Serve hot or refrigerate for 3 hours and enjoy the Red Velvet Halwa.

7

Eat to Prevent and
Control Arthritis

Arthritis is a joint disorder characterized by swelling with stiffness and joint pain. To prevent and control arthritis, your diet should be rich in foods that have the following activities:

· Foods that reduce inflammation.

· Foods that have potent antioxidant properties.

· Foods that modulate immune activity.

· Foods that balance the gut microbiome.

This chapter helps you include superfoods in your diet that have therapeutic effects and help prevent and manage arthritic conditions effectively.

Superfoods that prevent and control arthritis are:

Foods that reduce inflammation in the body through their anti-inflammatory and antioxidant properties: **Turmeric, horse gram, walnuts, mushrooms,** and **licorice root.**

Foods rich in omega-3 fatty acids: **Flax seeds, chia seeds,** and **soybean.**

Foods rich in calcium: **Chia seeds, sesame,** and **soybean.**

Foods rich in vitamin K: **Soybean, cabbage,** and **nuts.**

Pre-biotics foods that increase the good bacteria and crowd out pro-inflammatory bacteria in the gut: **Oats, garlic, onion, soybean, flax seeds, almonds,** and **cocoa powder.**

Mulethi Herbal Chai

Serves: 4 | Prep time: 5 mins | Cooking time: 15 mins | Beverage

Ingredients

Licorice root:	2 inches	Ashwagandha root:	2 inches
Cinnamon stick:	1 inch	Black Pepper:	8
Ginger:	1½ inches	Water:	800 ml

Method

1. Crush ginger, cinnamon, and black pepper using a pestle.
2. Add crushed herbs, licorice root, and ashwagandha root in water.
3. Bring it to a boil. Simmer for 10 minutes on medium flame till water reduces to 600 ml.
4. Strain the tea. The licorice root is enough to make tea sweet. No sweetener is needed to be added to it. Drink hot Mulethi Herbal Chai.

Fennel Chia Seeds Milk Shake

Serves: 4 | Prep time: 30 mins | Cooking time: 10 mins | Beverage

Ingredients

Skimmed milk:	1 L	Fennel:	5 tbsp
Honey:	If required	Almonds:	100 g
Water:	80 ml	Chia seeds:	2 tbsp

Method

1. Soak chia seeds in 80 ml water overnight or for at least 4 hours.
2. Soak almonds in hot water for half an hour. Remove the skin and blend it with milk (about 40 ml-60 ml) to make a thick cream. Keep it in the refrigerator for 2 hours to set the cream.
3. Wash the fennel seeds thoroughly. Dry on a kitchen towel for 20 minutes. Finely grind the fennel seeds.
4. Bring the milk to a boil. Turn the flame to low. Add fennel seeds powder and simmer for 5 minutes.
5. Turn off the flame and let it cool down. Strain the milk. Add honey, mix well and chill for 2 hours in the refrigerator.
6. Add almond cream into individual glasses. Add a spoonful of soaked chia seeds. Pour fennel milk and enjoy refreshing Fennel Chia Seeds Milk Shake.

Grilled Mushrooms

Serving: 4 | Prep time: 10 mins | Cooking time: 15 mins | Snack

Ingredients

Button mushrooms:	600 g	Black pepper powder:	1 tsp
Red chili powder:	¼ tsp	Extra virgin olive oil:	2 ½ tbsp
Salt:	To taste		

Method

1. Wash the mushrooms thoroughly and cut them into half an inch. Sprinkle salt, red chili powder, and black pepper powder.

2. Add oil and mix well. Spread the mushroom pieces on the baking tray. Make sure they do not overlap each other. If the quantity is more, grill/bake in 2 batches.

3. If you have grill function in your oven, grill the mushrooms in 2 batches for 15 minutes. Alternatively, bake in a pre-heated oven at 180°C for 15 minutes.

Oats Walnut Namkeen

Makes: 300 g | Prep time: 10 mins
Cooking time: 20 mins | Snack

Ingredients

Rolled oats:	200 g
Desiccated coconut:	25 g
Fennel:	1 tbsp
Sesame seeds:	2 tbsp
Almonds:	12
Pumpkin seeds:	2 tbsp
Asafoetida:	1 tsp
Turmeric powder:	1 tsp
Kashmiri red chili powder:	1 tbsp
Salt:	To taste
Walnuts:	40 g
Coriander seeds:	1 tbsp
Curry leaves:	20-25
Peanuts:	35 g
Pistachios:	10
Raisins:	2 tbsp
Garam masala:	½ tsp
Brown sugar:	1 ½ tbsp
Dry mango powder:	1 tsp

Method

1. Dry roast fennel seeds and coriander seeds and desiccated coconut till they start releasing an aromatic smell. Grind them coarsely in a mixer grinder. Keep the masala for later use.

2. Dry roast oats till they start changing color. Remove from heat.

3. Chop walnuts, almonds, and pistachios.

4. Heat oil in a pan. Add Asafoetida, sesame seeds in hot oil and cook for a minute.

5. Add curry leaves and peanuts. Roast for 5 minutes.

6. Add almonds, pistachios, pumpkin seeds, walnuts, and raisins one by one. Roast till they turn slightly brown.

7. Add turmeric powder, chili powder, salt, garam masala, and dry mango powder. Cook for a minute.

8. Add roasted rolled oats. Mix well.

9. Add prepared masala and brown sugar. Mix well.

10. Turn off the flame and leave the oats walnut namkeen in the pan till it cools down completely.

11. Enjoy Oats Walnut Namkeen with evening tea. Store the namkeen in an airtight container for up to 15 days.

Flax Seeds Spread

Makes: 110 g | **Prep time:** 10 mins | **Cooking time:** 10 mins | **Condiment**

Ingredients

Flax seeds:	30 g	Sesame seeds:	30 g
Garlic:	15-18 cloves	Dry red chilies:	2
Cumin seeds:	3 tsp	Lemon juice:	3 tsp
Extra virgin olive oil:	1 tsp	Salt:	To taste
Water:	60 ml		

Method

1. Dry roast flax seeds on low flame till flax seeds turn dark and slightly puffed up. Remove from heat.

2. Dry roast sesame seeds, cumin seeds, and red chilies till they slightly change color. Keep stirring to prevent the burning of seeds.

3. Grind all the ingredients together except olive oil to make a superfine spread. Add extra virgin olive oil and mix.

4. Apply flax seeds spread on toast and rolls or use as a dip or serve as chutney. Store it in the refrigerator and consume within 3 days.

Tip: Proper roasting of flax seeds is an important step to reduce the peculiar taste of flax seeds, so roast them until they become slightly puffed.

Mushroom Walnut Soup

Serves: 4 | Prep time: 5 mins | Cooking time: 20 mins | Starter

Ingredients

Sliced button mushroom:	500 g		Walnut kernels:	20
Garlic:	16-20 cloves		Ginger:	1½ inches
Onion:	2 medium		Sesame seeds:	1 tbsp
Cloves:	4		Garam masala powder:	¼-½ tsp
Black pepper powder:	½ tsp		Rock salt:	To taste
Curd:	2 tbsp		Water:	1500 ml
Sesame oil:	2 tbsp			

Method

1. Heat sesame oil in a pan. Add walnuts to it. Roast for 5 minutes or until they begin to change color. Remove walnuts from heat.

2. Roughly crush walnuts with the help of a pestle. Alternatively, grind 1 or 2 times in pulse mode. Do not grind walnuts to a fine powder, this will make walnuts bitter. Keep aside.

3. In the same oil, add sesame seeds and cloves. When they start crackling, add chopped ginger and garlic and cook for 2 minutes.

4. Add chopped onion and cook for 10 minutes.

5. Add sliced mushrooms. Cook for 5 minutes. Stir occasionally. Add rock salt and black pepper powder. Mix well and cook for 10 minutes. Take out 10 mushroom pieces for garnishing.

6. Add 250 ml of water and bring it to a boil. Simmer for 5 minutes.

7. When water is somewhat reduced, add another 250 ml of water. Bring it to a boil. Simmer for 5 minutes.

8. Turn the flame to low and add curd. Cook for 2-3 minutes.

9. Add another 250 ml of water. Bring it to a boil, then simmer for 5 minutes or until soup thickens.

10. Add ¼ tsp of garam masala. Add 250 ml water and repeat step 9.

11. Turn off the flame. Cool the soup and blend it into smooth soup in a blender. If required, add 250 to 300 ml of water while blending.

12. Bring the soup to heat. If the soup seems thick, add 200 ml of water. Taste and add ¼ tsp of garam masala if required. Bring it to a boil. Simmer for 5 minutes.

13. Turn off the flame. Pour soup in individual soup bowls. Add mushroom pieces and crushed walnuts. Mix and serve hot.

Tips:

1. It is necessary to add water gradually to make the soup rich in flavor. Adding all the water at once will make the soup thinner and bland.

2. A total of 1500 ml of water was used for this soup. Your water quantity can range from 1300 ml to 1600 ml. So, add water gradually and adjust the amount of water as needed.

3. Over time, the soup becomes thick and strong flavored. If you are storing the soup for later, add 200 ml of water, adjust seasoning, and bring it to a boil before serving.

Instant Turmeric Pickle

Makes: 150 g | Prep time: 15 mins | Condiment

Ingredients

Fresh turmeric:	150 g
Chopped Lemon:	2
Kala namak mix:	1 tbsp
Black pepper powder:	½ tsp
Lemon juice/ Amla juice:	2 tbsp
Asafoetida:	½ tsp
Cumin seeds powder:	½ tbsp
Mustard oil:	2 tbsp

Method

1. Wash turmeric thoroughly. Remove the skin. Finely chop them.
2. Add asafoetida, kala namak mix, cumin seeds powder, black pepper powder, mustard oil, and chopped lemon. Mix well.
3. Add lemon juice or amla juice. Mix well.
4. Spoon the mixture in a clean and dry jar. Cover the jar with a muslin cloth and keep it in sunlight for two days.
5. After two days, the turmeric pickle is ready to eat.
6. You can store turmeric pickles in the refrigerator for up to 1 week.

Horse Gram Dry Masala

Serves: 4 | Prep time: 10 mins | Cooking time: 30 mins | Side dish

Ingredients

Horse gram:	200 g	Cumin seeds:	½ tsp
Asafoetida:	½ tsp	Onion:	1 medium
Fenugreek seeds powder:	½ tsp	Chopped ginger-garlic:	1 tbsp
Tomato:	1 medium	Coriander powder:	1 tsp
Green chilies:	2	Cumin powder:	½ tsp
Garam masala:	¼ tsp	Bay leaf:	1
Mustard seeds:	½ tsp	Oil:	1 tbsp
Water:	200 ml		

Method

1. Soak horse gram overnight. Pressure cook horse gram with 200 ml water for 6 whistles.

2. Grind onion, ginger-garlic and green chilies with about 2 tbsp of water to make a thick and coarse paste. Grind tomatoes separately.

3. Heat oil in a pan. Add asafoetida, bay leaf, mustard seeds, and cumin seeds. Cook for 2 minutes. Add onion paste. Cook for 7 minutes.

4. Add tomatoes and salt. Cook for 5 minutes. Add fenugreek seeds, garam masala, cumin and coriander powder. Cook for 5-7 minutes.

5. Add horse gram with stock and salt. Mix well. If necessary, add more water. Cover with a lid and cook on low flame for 15 minutes.

6. Garnish with fresh coriander leaves and serve.

Soybean Masala

Serves: 4
Prep time: 10 mins
Cooking time: 45 mins
Main course

Method

1. Soak soybeans in enough water overnight. Wash soybeans, pressure cook them with salt and 450 ml water for 5-7 whistles.

2. Strain the soybeans. Keep the stock for later use.

3. Heat oil in a pressure cooker. Add asafoetida, cumin seeds, bay leaf, and cloves. Cook for a minute.

4. Add chopped ginger and garlic. Cook for 2 minutes. Add chopped onion. Cook for 10 minutes or until the onions are tender.

5. Add chopped tomatoes. Add salt, mix well and cook for 5 minutes.

6. Add turmeric powder, garam masala, coriander powder, and red chili powder. Mix well. Cover and cook on low flame for 10 minutes till the mixture starts releasing oil.

7. Add soybean. Mix well. Cook for 5-7 minutes. Add stock and pressure cook for 2 whistles.

8. Garnish with fresh coriander leaves. Enjoy it with chapati and rice.

Ingredients

Soybean:	300 g
Onion:	4 medium
Tomato:	3 medium
Ginger:	1½ inches
Garlic:	10 cloves
Bay leaf:	1
Cloves:	3
Cumin seeds:	½ tsp
Asafoetida:	1 tsp
Garam masala:	1 tsp
Turmeric powder:	½ tsp
Coriander powder:	1 tsp
Red chili powder:	1 tsp
Salt:	To taste
Water:	450 ml

Royal Horse Gram Dal Fry

Serves: 4 | Prep time: 10 mins | Cooking time: 30 mins | Main course

Ingredients

Horse gram:	250 g	Garlic:	8-10 cloves
Ginger:	1½ inches	Onion:	3 medium
Tomato:	3 medium	Asafoetida:	¼ tsp
Cumin seeds:	½ tsp	Bay leaf:	1
Turmeric powder:	½ tsp	Garam masala:	½ tsp
Coriander powder:	½ tsp	Water:	800 ml
Kashmiri red chili powder:	½ tsp	Salt:	To taste

Method

1. Soak horse gram overnight. Wash overnight soaked horse gram with fresh water and pressure cook with 500 ml water, salt, and turmeric powder on low-medium for 4 whistles.

2. Heat oil in a pan. Add asafoetida, bay leaf, and cumin seeds. Cook for a minute. Add chopped ginger and garlic. Cook for a minute.

3. Add chopped onion. Cook for 10 minutes. Add chopped tomatoes and salt. Cover and cook for 10 minutes.

4. Add garam masala, coriander powder and red chili powder and mix well. Cover and cook for 5 minutes.

5. Add horse gram along with stock and mix well. Add 300 ml of water and bring it to a boil. Mash 30% of dal fry with a masher. Cook on medium flame for 5 minutes.

6. Turn off the flame. Enjoy Royal Horse Gram Dal Fry with rice.

Cabbage Dry Fruit Roll

Makes: 18 rolls
Prep time: 20 mins
Cooking time: 40 mins
Dessert

Ingredients

Fresh Cabbage:	1 large
Jaggery:	80 g - 100 g
Clove:	3
Water:	500 ml
Licorice root:	2 inches

For Filling

Desiccated coconut:	60 g	Dates:	15 - 17
Walnut kernels:	4	Almonds:	10
Cashew nuts:	10	Pistachios:	10
Pumpkin seeds:	1 tbsp	Melon seeds:	1 tbsp
Rock salt:	A pinch	Ghee:	½ tsp

Method

For Filling

1. Remove the seeds from the dates. Mash the dates with a masher to make them smooth. If the dates are not soft enough, beat them with a pestle to make them smooth.

2. Chop all nuts. Heat ghee in a pan and add all nuts and seeds. Roast till nuts start turning a little brown.

3. Add desiccated coconut. Cook for 3-4 minutes.

4. Add dates and a pinch of rock salt. Mix well. Cook for 2-3 minutes until the dates are hot and soft and all the ingredients are combined. Turn off the flame and let it cool down for 5 minutes.

5. Grease your palm. Once the filling is cool enough to handle, make small laddoos. The laddoos need not be in perfect shape and should be slightly cylindrical in shape for easy rolling. Keep aside.

For Cabbage roll

1. Wash the cabbage thoroughly. Remove the first hard layer of leaves. Make a horizontal cut at the bottom of the cabbage and carefully take out the cabbage leaves. Repeat the step to collect 9 cabbage leaves.

2. Put jaggery, licorice root, cloves, and water in a pan. Bring it to the boil. Simmer for 3-4 minutes.

3. When the syrup starts to thicken a bit, add cabbage leaves. Add 1 or 2 leaves at a time. Keep the flame on medium-high and cook for 5-8 minutes until the cabbage becomes soft and absorbs the flavor. Take out the cabbage from the syrup.

4. Repeat the process for all the cabbage leaves. Turn off the flame. Allow the cabbage to air dry for 2-3 minutes.

5. Cut the cabbage leaves vertically into two halves. If the leaves are too large, cut them into 3 pieces.

6. Place a laddoo at one end of the cabbage. Roll the cabbage. No need to seal the ends, when the cabbage will dry, the ends will stick together automatically.

7. Make all the cabbage rolls. Refrigerate for two hours and serve.

Walnut Choco Chia Seeds Pudding

Serves: 4 | Prep time: 40 mins | Cooking time: 10 mins | Dessert

Ingredients

Chia seeds:	10 tbsp		Milk:	1 L
Overnight soaked walnuts:	10		Cocoa powder:	3 tbsp
Honey:	2 tbsp or to taste		Licorice root:	2 inches
			Nutmeg:	½ small
Cinnamon:	2 inches		Water:	50 ml
Cashew nuts:	100 g		Chocolate shaving:	4 tbsp
Dry roasted walnuts:	2 tbsp			

Method

1. Soak cashew nuts in 50 ml of hot water for 15 minutes. Blend cashews with stock to make a smooth cream. Refrigerate for 2 hours to set the cream.

2. Add cocoa powder, cinnamon, nutmeg, and licorice root to the milk. Bring it to a boil. Simmer for 5-7 minutes on low flame.

3. Turn off the flame. Cover and let it cool for 10 minutes.

4. Remove cinnamon stick, nutmeg, and licorice root. Add overnight soaked walnuts and blend until smooth.

5. Take out the flavored milk in a bowl. Add chia seeds, honey and mix vigorously. Leave for 20 minutes to allow chia seeds to swell up.

6. Mix again and break any lumps. Pour the pudding into individual jars. Chill in the refrigerator overnight or at least for 5-6 hours.

7. Add cashew cream, chocolate shavings, roasted walnuts on top and serve.

Flax Seeds Laddoo

Makes: 25 units | Prep time: 30 mins | Cooking time: 20 mins | Dessert

Ingredients

Flax seeds:	500 g	Cow's ghee:	2 tbsp
Chopped almonds:	100 g	Chopped walnuts:	100 g
Jaggery:	250 g	Tragacanth gum/ gond:	100 g (optional)

Method

1. Dry roast the flax seeds on low flame till their color changes slightly.
2. Let the roasted flax seeds cool down and grind them in a grinder.
3. Grate the jaggery and keep aside.
4. Heat ghee in a pan. Cook gond in the ghee till it swells.
5. Take out the gond from the ghee. Let it cool and break it with a pestle or your hand.
6. Add nuts to the remaining ghee. Roast till they turn slightly brown.
7. Take out the nuts and add grated jaggery in the same ghee.
8. Cook for 3-5 minutes till jaggery melts. Turn off the flame immediately. Don't cook jaggery after it dissolves, or else laddoos will be hard to chew. Add the flax seeds, nuts and gond. Mix well.
9. Make round shape laddoo with hands while the mixture is still hot.
10. If laddoos are not binding well, then heat the mixture for 2 minutes.
11. Enjoy Flax Seeds Laddoos. Store the remaining laddoos in the refrigerator and consume them within two weeks.

8
Quick
Shorties

Carrot-White Radish Instant Pickle: Chop 100 g carrot and 100 g radish. Add 1 tbsp panch phoran, 1 tbsp mustard oil, and ½ tbsp apple cider vinegar. Add salt and mix well. Eat with dal-rice.

Green Garlic Pickle: Chop 100 g green garlic and 2 green chilies and crush them in a mortar with a pestle. Similarly, crush 2 inches of ginger. Add 1 tsp mustard oil and salt to taste and mix well.

Raw Papaya Chutney: Peel and grate 100 g raw papaya. Add salt, 1 tsp Kashmiri red chili powder, 1 tbsp brown sugar, ½ tsp coriander powder, and 1 tbsp extra virgin olive oil. Mix well.

Anti-flatulence Churn: Dry roast 1 tsp carom seeds, 1 tsp fenugreek seeds, and ½ tsp asafetida. Add black salt. Cool and grind them. Take half teaspoon of churn for belching and flatulence when required.

Arthritis Churn: Dry roast 50 g carom seeds, 25 g fenugreek seeds, and 5 g caraway. Grind them to make a coarse powder. Take half teaspoon of this churn with lukewarm water at night. Store it in an airtight container.

Digestion Booster: Take a teaspoon each of coriander seeds, cumin seeds, and fennel. Soak them overnight in a glass of water. Drink this water in the morning to boost digestion in summer when required.

Spicy Toffee (For cough and sore throat): Crush ginger (2 inches) and 10 black pepper with a pestle. Add 10 g jaggery and 1 tsp cow ghee. Mix all ingredients and cook for 3 minutes. Take it as a toffee 2 times a day for cough and sore throat.

Fenugreek Water: Soak 1 tsp of fenugreek seeds in water overnight. Drink this fenugreek water in the morning on an empty stomach. Do it every day to control diabetes.

About The Author

With a Master's Degree in Pharmacy, the author La Fonceur is a research scientist and registered pharmacist. She specialized in Pharmaceutical Technology and worked as a research scientist in the pharmaceutical research and development department. She is a health blogger and a dance artist. Her previous books include *Eat to Prevent and Control Disease, Secret of Healthy Hair,* and *Eat So What!* series. Being a research scientist, she has worked closely with drugs, and based on her experience, she believes that one can prevent most of the diseases with nutritious vegetarian foods and a healthy lifestyle.

READ MORE FROM LA FONCEUR

Hindi Editions

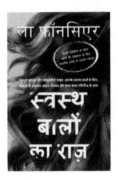

CONNECT WITH LA FONCEUR

 @la_fonceur | @eatsowhat   @la_fonceur

 LaFonceur | eatsowhat   @eatsowhat

Sign up to get exclusive offers on La Fonceur books:

Blog: www.eatsowhat.com

Website: www.lafonceur.com/sign-up

Join La Fonceur mailing list at www.eatsowhat.com/mailing-list

Ingram Content Group UK Ltd.
Milton Keynes UK
UKHW020954080323
418216UK00006B/221

9 798210 557278